Swansea Psychiatric Education Centre
01792-516568

This book is due f

LAW AND GENERAL PRACTICE

by
Chris Hughes MA, MSc, CBiol, MIBiol

**Solicitor, and Head of Legal Services,
British Medical Association**

**Doral House • 2(b) Manor Road
Beckenham • Kent • BR3 2LE**

ACKNOWLEDGEMENTS

To Vera and Joe, my mother and father,
who have given me so much, for so long.

ISBN
1 873839 09 X

Further copies of *Law and General Practice* may be obtained from Pi books, a division of Publishing Initiatives (Europe) Ltd, price £19.95 (ex. VAT). This publication reflects the view and experience of the author, and not necessarily those of Publishing Initiatives (Europe) Ltd.

FOREWORD

The work of a general practitioner is challenging rather than mundane. Every time the consulting room door opens something new is presented. This is truly the 'sharp end' of medicine. It is stimulating to be faced with these challenges, gratifying to gain experience and confidence with time, and satisfying to build up long-term relationships with patients and their families.

We forget about less rewarding aspects of our job until we are forced to face up to them. The unwelcome truth is that general practitioners are increasingly vulnerable to legal challenges, coming not only from patients and their families but also from statutory bodies and the General Medical Council. Knowledge of the law as it affects us, our contract with the Family Health Services Authority, and our responsibility towards our patients and staff, is becoming even more important if we wish to avoid getting into difficulties. Most GPs, if threatened with legal action, would be surprised - and horrified. Questions would need to be anwered. What did I do wrong? Did I make a mistake? Is this the result of misunderstanding, or of poor communication? Could the situation have been foreseen? Most importantly, how can I prevent anything like this happening again?

The Hippocratic oath is familiar to all doctors, and much of the behaviour that is expected of us is based on this. How is it that every year a number of GPs are found guilty of breaking one of its rules? When a doctor is appointed as a principal by the FHSA, he/she signs a contract. Why is it that every GP can expect to appear before a Medical Service Committee at least once, and may be found in breach of that contract as a result? And do all GPs ensure that those they employ are properly trained for their jobs, in the knowledge that the GP is responsible for the actions of staff if they get it wrong?

There is also a sense that the citizen of the 1990s is less reticent about suing the GP. Whether this will become as common here as elsewhere remains to be seen, but the threat is there. The personal understanding between the patient and the GP reduces the risk, but with a move towards larger practices and more delegation of patient care to others in a multiprofessional team, this may change.

The comprehensive range of information provided in this concise and readable book, with its commonsense approach and absence of 'legal jargon', will guide the new GP and existing practice staff through what may seem at first a minefield of traps for the unwary and unprepared. It contains much that the more experienced GP will find useful, and certainly a lot of information, for example on employment and health and safety law, that that will be valuable for all members of the primary health-care team. If this book is on the practice shelf for all to read, many of the legal hazards of general practice today will be avoided.

Ann Orme-Smith FRCGP
GP, Tadworth, Surrey

CONTENTS

RELEVANT ACTS AND REGULATIONS

Coroners Act 1887

National Health Service Act 1946

Occupiers Liability Act 1957

Health and Safety at Work Act 1974

Sex Discrimination Act 1975

Race Relations Act 1976

National Health Service Act 1977

Employment Protection
(Consolidation) Act 1978

Nurses, Midwives and Health Visitors
Act 1979

Supreme Court Act 1981

Medical Act 1983

Mental Health Act 1983

Data Protection Act 1984

Police and Criminal Evidence
Act 1984

Reporting of Injuries, Diseases and
Dangerous Occurrences
Regulations 1985

Wages Act 1986

Consumer Protection Act 1987

Nurses, Midwives and Health Visitors
(Professional Conduct) Rules 1987

Access to Medical Reports Act 1988

Control of Substances Hazardous to
Health Regulations 1988

Children Act 1989

Access to Health Records Act 1990

National Health Service and
Community Care Act 1990

NHS (General Medical Services)
Regulations 1992

NHS (Service Committees and
Tribunal) Regulations 1992

Display Screen Equipment at Work
Regulations 1993

Management and Use of Work
Equipment Regulations 1993

Management of Health and Safety at
Work Regulations 1993

Manual Handling Regulations 1993

Personal Protective Equipment at
Work Regulations 1993

Trade Union Reform and
Employment Rights Act 1993

Work Place (Health, Safety and
Welfare) Regulations 1993

Medical Devices Regulations 1994

INTRODUCTION

LAW AND WHERE IT COMES FROM

One definition of law is that it is the set of definable and enforceable rules by which a sovereign group of individuals regulates its affairs. In plain language, British law is the set of rules that are enforced by the courts in Britain.

The UK is a country rich in law - too rich. The standard summary (*Halsbury's Laws of England*) of English law is about 55,000 pages long - and it is only a summary. This is, however, supplemented by an approximately equal length of statute law and a greater bulk of Statutory Instruments. But this is not the complete story; the law in Scotland is in many respects different, and that in Northern Ireland is different again. The Channel Islands and the Isle of Man also have their own individual legal systems. In practice, all these systems are, to a greater or lesser extent, similar in their detailed provisions.

Obviously, no individual could possibly 'know' any more than a tiny fragment of all this; nor does anyone need to. Lawyers usually know quite a lot about one small area of law, and have a general understanding of rather more. Most importantly, they know how to investigate a legal problem, and how to research the answer using standard texts such as *Halsbury's Laws*.

Law is derived from a variety of different sources. The most basic is **customary law,** which consists of the accepted rules of a primitive society. As a society develops and has new needs, it adds new laws to this system and some old laws fall away. In English law, these rights and rules are the original basis for the **criminal law** and the **law of tort** (which deals, for example, with the right to compensation after an accident). Another source of law which has grown up over the centuries is the terms on which merchants buy and sell - the **law of contract.** Over time, these have formed the mass of English law known as 'common law', which consists of the decisions judges have made in the past when cases have come before the courts, which have transformed customary law into '**judge-made**' law.

One area of common law which continues to develop and is of great importance in everyday life is that part of the law of tort called **negligence.** In order for individual A to claim compensation for injury from individual B, s/he has to show that B was under an obligation to be careful not to harm him/her (owed him/her a duty of care), that B failed to take proper steps to ensure that s/he did not cause harm (breach of the duty of care - i.e. careless or negligent), and as a result, A suffered harm of a degree which should be compensated.

However, this system of law-making, even though it does allow the law to evolve, is not adequate to deal with the sort of complex society which has evolved. Law has to be invented to deal with the needs of society. For the past 800 years this process of the conscious invention of law has been done by the

Monarch in Council and then by Parliament, and is called **legislation**. The system developed involves Parliament passing laws (statutes), or giving limited law-making powers to Ministers and others who make the law under this delegated power (statutory instruments, regulations, bye-laws etc.).

From the Middle Ages to the end of the 19th century, there were two systems of courts running in parallel. In addition to the courts that enforced the common law and statutory law, there was a system of courts of conscience - the 'courts of equity'. These could, in certain cases, intervene to enforce principles of fairness, and supplemented the common law where failure to do so would result in injustice. These courts developed the law of confidentiality, and of wills and trusts. Now all civil courts apply both the common law and equity.

In 1973, the UK joined the various organisations now known as the European Union. As a result of this, the UK is now part of a larger society in which some law-making is done on a European basis rather than simply for the UK.

THE LAW IN GENERAL PRACTICE

General practice is subject to the same body of laws as the rest of society. The amount of law which potentially has an impact on workers in general practice is therefore considerable. However, the purpose of this book is to provide a clear guide to those areas of law which have a day-to-day significance for this kind of work, to enable the reader to work effectively and confidently in this setting, and thus make a full contribution to work in primary care.

The law covered in this book is from all the main sources discussed above, and a few more besides. While most of it is of general applicability, some of it (for example the specific provisions of the regulations under which NHS general practice is provided) relates only to general practice. Other aspects of law dealt with (for example the duty of confidentiality or questions of health and safety at work), while being common to all business relationships, are of greater importance in a clinical setting and have aspects which are unique.

THE STRUCTURE OF THE BOOK

Chapter 1 considers the obligations and responsibilities of GPs, the varying systems for enforcing those duties and the consequences of breach of duty. The practical role of support staff in discharging these responsibilities is stressed.

Chapter 2 deals with the general range of medical and nursing ethics, why they exist, where they come from and how they are enforced, together with questions of fitness to practice.

Chapter 3 discusses, in rather more depth, key questions of ethics and law - consent to treatment, the patient's right to confidentiality, consent and confidentiality for treating children, questions concerning patients' records, and mental health.

Chapter 4 provides a summary of the law pertaining to negligent actions in relation to medical practice, and the statutory framework for actions arising from product liability.

Chapter 5 provides an overview of the provisions of employment law. It focuses on the contract of employment, and how it defines the working relationship and obligations of employer and employee. It then considers disciplinary procedures in a general practice setting, discrimination law and maternity rights.

Chapter 6 deals with the responsibility of employer and employee to ensure that the working environment is safe.

Chapter 7 deals with relations with the judicial process and solicitors, and in particular the role of the doctor as an expert or professional witness.

Chapter 8 looks at relationships with the media and the constraints imposed on doctors by the law of defamation, as well as the interactions of their professional duties to their colleagues and the public in their statements.

Chapter 9 looks at the 'rights' of the patient set out in the *Patients' Charter*; it deals with their origins and the role of the Charter.

The book concludes with a summary of the responsibilities of the NHS and various other bodies concerned with general practice, and suggestions for further reading.

Chapter 1

THE GP AND THE NATIONAL HEALTH SERVICE

THE LEGAL FRAMEWORK OF GENERAL PRACTICE

The National Health Service (NHS) was brought into existence by the *NHS Act* 1946. Since then, there has been a continual process of change and development, and frequent Acts of Parliament to implement them. Most of the key provisions in statute law relating to the health service are contained in the *NHS Act* 1977 (and its Scottish and Northern Irish equivalents) and the *NHS and Community Care Act* 1990.

Section 1 of the *NHS Act* 1977 requires the Secretary of State to continue the promotion of a comprehensive health service designed to secure improvement in the health of the people, and in the prevention, diagnosis and treatment of illness. Other provisions set out the structure and responsibilities of the various sorts of health authorities which have the job of organising the day-to-day provision of services. Section 29(1) provides:

> *'It is the duty of every Family Health Services Authority, in accordance with the regulations, to arrange as respects·their locality with medical practitioners to provide personal medical services for all persons in the locality who wish to take advantage of the arrangements. The services so provided are in this Act referred to as "general medical services".'*

The regulations are now contained in the *NHS (General Medical Services) Regulations* 1992, made by the Secretary of State for Health under powers contained in the *NHS Act* 1977. These terms of service have been negotiated over many years between the Department of Health (DoH) and the General Medical Services Committee (GMSC) on behalf of the medical profession. They are the framework within which GPs work, as they determine how a doctor can come to practise in any area, what his/her terms of service are and how s/he is paid. The payments are made in accordance with the *Statement of Fees and Allowances* (commonly known as the 'Red Book'), published by the Secretary of State.

NHS GPS' OBLIGATIONS TO THEIR PATIENTS

At any time, a GP has a list of patients which is kept by the Family Health Services Authority (FHSA); apart from those treated under temporary or emergency arrangements, these are the patients for whom s/he is responsible. These are the people who have chosen to be treated by that GP and have been accepted onto the list, or who have been allocated to the GP by the FHSA. Where a GP accepts a patient or removes one from the list, it is important that the FHSA is notified quickly so that there is no uncertainty as to who is, and who is not, a patient.

Although NHS general practice is the subject of much law and regulation, there is no definition of what general practice is. Paragraph 12 of the *Terms of Services* states that:

> *'a doctor shall render to his patients all necessary and appropriate medical services of the type usually provided by general medical practitioners.'*

This failure to define 'appropriate medical services' reflects the complexity and changing nature of general practice. It states, in effect, that 'general practice is what general practitioners do'. This definition emphasises the importance of the regulation of the profession by the profession. An individual doctor can in theory be in breach of his/her terms of service if s/he fails to deliver the services which his/her colleagues provide. It is a modern example of what was discussed in the Introduction - the law giving effect to the established and accepted customs of society.

However, while the *Terms of Service* do contain this 'sweeping up' statement, they also list many specific duties which a GP is obliged to perform (see Figure 1).

FIGURE 1 - THE GP'S SERVICES TO PATIENTS

Under the *Terms of Service*, a GP is required to:

(1) Give general advice on the patient's health and with reference to diet, exercise, tobacco, alcohol and misuse of drugs and solvents.

(2) Offer patients consultations and appropriate examinations to identify or reduce the risk of disease and injury.

(3) Offer and provide vaccination or immunisation against measles, mumps, rubella, pertussis, Hib, poliomyelitis, diphtheria and tetanus.

(4) Make appropriate referrals for the provision of other services under the NHS Act.

(5) Give appropriate advice to help patients get services from the local authority social services department.

(6) Offer a health check to elderly patients, and provide a check for new patients or patients not seen within three years if requested.

(7) Attend and treat a patient who attends during surgery hours.

(8) Issue certain certificates to patients. Prescribe drugs needed for the treatment of the patient in accordance with the *Terms and Conditions of Service*.

(9) Provide home visits if the condition of the patient so requires.

(Drawn from paragraphs 12,13, 14, 15, 16, 37 and 43 of the Terms of Service)

In addition, appropriately qualified GPs may provide other services to patients - child health surveillance, contraceptive services, maternity medical services or minor surgery.

In providing any of these services, the GP is clearly under a duty to provide a good service. In doing so s/he must not act negligently. This means that s/he must act with the care, skill and diligence appropriate to a reasonable GP. A doctor does not guarantee the result of treatment; simply because treatment is unsuccessful does not mean that the doctor has failed to do the job properly. A doctor is not guilty of negligence if s/he has acted in accordance with a practice accepted as correct by a responsible body of medical practitioners skilled in that particular form of treatment, even if there is another body of opinion opposed to that practice. Clearly, no doctor can be an expert in every aspect of clinical practice. By definition, a GP does not set out to be the world's expert in, for example, heart disease. A GP is expected to be competent at general practice, and if s/he provides additional services s/he should provide them competently. The definition of the quality of service is provided by paragraph 3 of the *Terms of Service* (Figure 2).

FIGURE 2 - QUALITY OF SERVICE A GENERAL PRACTITIONER PROVIDES

'Where a decision whether any, and if so what, action is to be taken under these Terms of Service requires the exercise of professional judgement, a doctor shall not, in reaching that decision, be expected to exercise a higher degree of skill, knowledge and care than:

(a) in the case of a doctor providing child health surveillance services under Regulation 28, maternity medical services under Regulation 31 or minor surgery services under Regulation 33, which any general practitioner included in the child health surveillance list, the obstetric list or, as the case may be, the minor surgery list may reasonably be expected to exercise; and

(b) in any other case, that which general practitioners as a class may reasonably be expected to exercise.'

(Paragraph 3 of the Terms of Service for General Practitioners.)

This statutory definition of what is an acceptable standard of care is therefore a re-statement of the duty of care that doctors owe to their patients in the tort of negligence, and they must always use the level of skill which is expected of GPs. A failure to meet this standard, which causes harm to a patient, exposes the GP to the risk of a claim for damages or, in very extreme circumstances, to a prosecution for manslaughter.

GPS' RESPONSIBILITIES TO AND FOR THEIR STAFF

Although the major issues of GP/staff relations are dealt with in later chapters, the *Terms of Service* do lay certain specific responsibilities on GPs with respect to their staff.

Paragraph 17 requires doctors to treat patients who attend during surgery hours. If an appointments system operates and a patient attends without an appointment, then the doctor may refuse to see the patient then and there.

However, the patient has to be offered a reasonable appointment and the patient's health must not be put in danger; in addition, *a doctor shall take reasonable steps to ensure that no refusal is made without his knowledge'*. In order for a doctor to be able to do this, good and effective communication between the staff and the GP is essential.

Paragraph 28 obliges GPs, before taking on any member of staff, to make sure that the individual is suitably qualified and competent to do the job. It also requires them to give all employees opportunities for training to maintain their competence.

The training and competence of a GP's employees is of crucial significance to the GP for many obvious reasons. An employer is responsible in law for the actions of an employee under the principle of **vicarious liability**. A GP will almost always be held responsible in law if something goes wrong in the care of a patient resulting from a failure by one of his/her employees. This could mean a claim for damages, a service committee hearing or disciplinary proceedings before the General Medical Council (GMC).

GPS' OBLIGATIONS TO THE FHSA

In addition to those responsibilities concerning individual patients considered above, the NHS GP undertakes numerous other responsibilities to the FHSA. These may be summarised as ensuring that there are appropriate arrangements with respect to practice premises and the availability of care, and providing information to the FHSA.

Under the NHS system, a GP receives various payments from the FHSA depending on such things as the number of patients and their ages, the level of service provided, the costs of employing staff and other expenses relating to the practice. In order to ensure that the correct payments are made, the GP submits regular claims; as these are accounting documents, it is essential that these are accurate and timely. In addition, GPs keep clinical records with respect to each patient's illness and treatment, provide annual reports to the FHSA, respond to individual inquiries from the FHSA about certification of illness, prescriptions and referrals, and publish practice leaflets.

The *NHS (Service Committees and Tribunal) Regulations* 1992 are the provisions which come into effect when matters go wrong. These require the FHSA to investigate when any allegation of a breach of a GP's terms of service is made by a patient, or on his/her behalf. If the matter is not resolved informally, then the GP may be summoned before a service committee which will decide whether or not there was such a breach and, if so, what action to take against the doctor. This can involve a warning, a withholding of money (in effect a fine) or other actions.

ACCOUNTABILITY TO THE COURTS AND THE GMC

A doctor who negligently causes injury to a patient (whether NHS or private) may be sued by that patient for the harm caused. These proceedings will be heard in the High Court or County Court, and the GP will be represented by his/her medical defence organisation. After the death of a patient, a GP may occasionally give evidence to a Coroner's Court at an inquest looking into the circumstances of the death (see Chapter 7). In certain very extreme cases, where it is alleged that a doctor did not have the consent of the patient (see Chapter 3) to an operation or where the treatment was so reckless that it caused death, a doctor may face criminal charges arising out of his/her practice.

In providing services, a doctor is obliged to comply with the general law. In particular, GPs must not, in providing services, unlawfully discriminate on the grounds of race or sex. This means that GPs must not refuse or fail to provide a service, or fail to provide a service of the same quality, or in the same way, to one person as they would to another of a different sex, marital status, race or nationality. This is also a fundamental question of professional ethics (Chapter 2), and discrimination is also important in employment law (Chapter 5).

All doctors practising in the UK are obliged by law to be registered with the General Medical Council. The basic role of the GMC is the maintenance of registers of medical practitioners who are fit to practise. It does this by supervising the education of doctors, registering them, advising them (by the publication of guidance, in particular the 'Blue Book' which deals with ethical matters), and by erasing, suspending or imposing conditions on their registration in the event of serious ill-health or misconduct (Chapter 2).

Chapter 2

MEDICAL AND NURSING ETHICS

MEDICAL ETHICS

Medicine is a profession, and as such it requires a prolonged period of training as well as mental ability. Professionals are expected to abide by high standards for their own sake, especially in respect of confidentiality (Chapter 3). They also owe a wider duty to the community, which may conflict with their duty to a particular patient. As professionals, doctors have to belong to the GMC, which sets standards for the profession on questions of conduct and ethics. Doctors, by their special knowledge, training and responsibilities, are in a position of considerable power and influence with respect to their patients.

Hand in hand with the responsibility of being a member of a profession, there is the obligation to behave in accordance with professional standards. All professions (doctors, lawyers, accountants, engineers etc.) lay down codes of conduct which members of the profession are expected to adhere to. One of the key responsibilities of a profession is to ensure that such codes are respected by their members; if they are not, then it is the profession's obligation to discipline and even, on occasion, to withdraw the right of an individual to practise. This chapter considers broad questions of ethics, in the next chapter consideration is given to some specific problem areas.

The first code of conduct for doctors dates back about 4,000 years; the Hippocratic Oath dates back about 2,500 years. There have been many other codes drafted since then. Many of the provisions of these seem strange to modern eyes, although there are some matters in old codes which are strikingly familiar:

> *'I will not cut for stone, even for patients in whom the disease is manifest;*
> *I will leave this operation to be performed by practitioners.'*

This stark demarcation between medicine and surgery reflected and influenced a division which continued for nearly all recorded history and (in a more benign form) still has influence. However, fundamental principles enunciated by Hippocrates still resonate:

> *'I will prescribe regimen for the good of my patients according to my*
> *ability and my judgement and never do harm to anyone. To please no one*
> *will I prescribe a deadly drug, nor give advice which may cause his death.*
> *All that may come to my knowledge in the exercise of my profession or*
> *outside of my profession or in daily commerce with men, which ought not*
> *to be spread abroad, I will keep secret and will never reveal.'*

Since the Second World War, and the concern about the activities of some doctors under the Nazis, there has been an international code of ethics for doctors (see Figure 3).

It is not possible to make a full and exhaustive statement of what medical ethics consists of. It is constantly evolving in response to the pressures of society and the thinking of doctors. The Geneva Declaration, as drafted in 1949, clearly no longer reflects contemporary attitudes to abortion. Some argue that, whatever

FIGURE 3 - THE DECLARATION OF GENEVA

- I solemnly pledge myself to consecrate my life to the service of humanity.

- I will give to my teachers the respect and gratitude which is their due.

- I will practise my profession with conscience and dignity.

- The health of my patient will be my first consideration.

- I will respect the secrets which are confided in me.

- I will maintain by all means in my power the honour and the noble traditions of the medical profession.

- My colleagues will be my brothers.

- I will not permit considerations of religion, nationality, race, party politics or social standing between my duty and my patients.

- I will maintain the utmost respect for human life from the time of conception.

- Even under threat, I will not use my medical knowledge contrary to the laws of humanity.

(World Medical Association 1949)

the ethical rules may be, there will always be circumstances in which, while the letter of the law is obeyed, the all-important spirit of the law may be broken.

Much modern thinking of medical ethics specifies four principles: beneficence, non-maleficence, autonomy and justice (Table 1).

Doctors in the UK are regulated and registered by the General Medical Council. After appropriate professional training, an individual qualifies as a doctor and is entitled to registration. After that, the doctor's conduct is liable to review by the GMC, which will intervene in certain circumstances.

The Professional Conduct Committee of the GMC considers the case of any medical practitioner who is convicted in the British Isles of a criminal offence or who is judged by the Committee to have been guilty of serious professional misconduct. If the GMC thinks fit, it may erase the doctor's name from the register (which means s/he is no longer a doctor), suspend the registration for up to 12 months or impose conditions for up to three years on the doctor's practice.

Disciplinary findings within the NHS by a Medical Service Committee or another body do not amount to a conviction; however, a charge of misconduct may arise out of the facts which have already been considered by such an NHS body.

Many cases referred to the GMC are disposed of at an early stage by a warning letter or a letter of advice - for example, in connection with a minor motoring offence or where a doctor's professional conduct has fallen below the

TABLE 1. THE FOUR PRINCIPLES OF MEDICAL ETHICS.

1. **Autonomy**	This means the right of a patient to control his own treatment, and the need of the doctor to have the consent of the patient before he starts treating (special rules apply to children or under circumstances where an individual is not able to give consent).
2. **Beneficence**	The doctor is under an obligation to confer benefits and prevent harm to the patient, and in any action must weigh up possible good and possible harm to the patient.
3. **Non-maleficence**	A doctor must not use his/her power or skill to injure or harm a patient.
4. **Justice**	Where there are scarce resources of care available to patients, giving care by the best and fairest means.

proper standard, but not so far as to necessitate a full enquiry before the Professional Conduct Committee.

The GMC advises that: '*any abuse of the privileges and opportunities afforded to a doctor or any grave dereliction of professional duty or serious breach of medical ethics may give rise to a charge of serious professional misconduct*'.

The key responsibility of a doctor is with respect to the proper care of a patient. The Council may institute proceedings when a doctor appears to have failed seriously in his/her professional duties, for example by failing to provide necessary treatment for a patient. In general practice, this question is most likely to arise where a doctor has failed to visit a patient or to see a patient who has presented him/herself at surgery. These are often matters which are the cause of complaint to service committees. It is, therefore, essential that general practitioners have adequate means of ensuring that all requests for visits are properly considered, and also that the provisions of paragraph 17 of the *Terms of Service* are complied with by practice staff.

In discharging their responsibilities to patients, doctors rely on their staff. Obviously, this delegation of certain medical duties is to nursing staff who have been trained to perform specialist functions. A doctor who does delegate must be satisfied that it is proper to delegate this activity, and that the person actually carrying out the treatment or procedure is competent to carry it out; the doctor retains ultimate responsibility for the care of the patient and is responsible if anything goes wrong.

Other areas of concern for the GMC include the improper prescription or supply of controlled drugs. There are clear statutory provisions regulating how such drugs are prescribed and requiring adequate records to be kept. When doctors sign medical certificates, they are under an obligation to take care to ensure that what they are signing is actually true. A doctor who signed a statement which was untrue, misleading or in any way improper, or who broke the law on drugs, might be liable to disciplinary proceedings.

Other areas of particular concern to the GMC include breach of professional confidence, some personal relationships between doctors and patients, improper influence in order to obtain money, abuse of alcohol or drugs, dishonesty, and indecent or violent behaviour.

Professional misconduct

The General Medical Council (GMC), through the Professional Conduct Committee, has the power to erase, make subject to conditions, or suspend, the registration of a doctor found guilty of serious professional misconduct. In this context, the usual matters of misconduct considered by the GMC are allegations of improper behaviour which bring the profession into disrepute. This would cover such matters as fraud, violence, drunkenness and inappropriate sexual conduct, especially with patients. The question of sexual relations with patients has long been recognised as professionally problematic. The Hippocratic Oath included:

'In every house where I come I will enter only for the good of my patients, keeping myself far from all intentional ill-doing and all seduction, and especially from the pleasures of love with women or with men, be they free or slaves.'

There is a considerable research literature (predominantly of American origin) on this ethical problem, and questions of improper sexual advances frequently figure in complaints to the GMC.

NURSING ETHICS

Like medicine, nursing is a profession which is regulated by members of the profession in the interests of the profession and the public. Nurses have similar codes of ethics and are subject to similar disciplinary proceedings as doctors. The issues faced by nurses and doctors in considering their professional and ethical responsibilities are essentially the same. In the UK, the regulation of nurses is carried out by the United Kingdom Central Council for Nursing, Midwifery and Health Visiting (UKCC).

This statutory body has similar procedures to the GMC, and can suspend or terminate the registration of a member of the profession for misconduct which is defined as: *'conduct unworthy as a registered nurse, midwife or health visitor'*. In addition, action may be taken against a professional where it is demonstrated that the fitness to practise of such a practitioner is seriously impaired by illness. In considering issues of misconduct, the UKCC has to determine what its standard for judgement is: *'the standard which the Committee takes as its yardstick is not the highest standard which a professional person might obtain, but a standard which can reasonably be expected of an average practitioner'.*

The UKCC *Code of Professional Conduct for the Nurse, Midwife and Health Visitor* is the definitive statement of the general professional obligations of nurses in the UK. Among its key requirements are obligations shown in Figure 4.

FIGURE 4 - KEY UKCC REQUIREMENTS FOR NURSES

Nurses are obliged to:

•'Act always in such a way as to promote and safeguard the well-being and interest of patients/clients.'

•'Ensure that no action or omission on his/her part within his/her sphere of influence is detrimental to the condition of patients/clients.'

•'Acknowledge any limitations of competence and refuse in such cases to accept delegated functions without first having received instruction in regard to those functions and having been assessed as competent.'

•'Respect confidential information obtained in the course of professional practice and refrain from disclosing such information without the consent of the patient/client or the person entitled to act on his/her behalf, except where disclosure is required by law or by the order of the court, or is necessary in the public interest.'

(From the UKCC Code of Professional Conduct for the Nurse, Midwife and Health Visitor)

The UKCC emphasises the need for nurses to ensure that they act in a professional way and do not allow their responsibilities as employees to override their professional duty.

In considering any case, the UKCC will look at all the facts surrounding it, including the personal circumstances of the nurse concerned and the nurse's overall conduct and behaviour (Table 2).

FITNESS TO PRACTISE

Doctors should have the insight to recognise that, like everyone else, they may become ill and need help. A crucial element of health care is the involvement of the sympathetic but dispassionate outsider who is in a position to consider objectively the needs of the individual. It is for this reason that informed professional opinion is opposed to self-treatment and doctors should, where possible, avoid treating members of their own families. When a doctor seeks treatment from a colleague s/he is entitled to the same care, concern and confidentiality as any other patient.

TABLE 2. REASONS WHY NURSES HAVE BEEN REMOVED FROM THE UKCC REGISTER.

- Reckless and wilfully unskilful practice.
- Concealing untoward incidents.
- Failure to keep essential records.
- Falsifying records.
- Failure to protect or promote the interests of patients.
- Failing to act knowing that a colleague or subordinate is improperly treating or abusing patients.
- Physical or verbal abuse of patients.
- Abuse of patients by improperly withholding prescribed drugs, or administering unprescribed drugs or an excess of prescribed drugs.
- Theft from patients or employers.
- Drug-related offences.
- Sexual abuse of patients.
- Breach of confidentiality.

CASE STUDY 1 - HIV INFECTION

Two practising GPs were being treated for HIV infection. This information was communicated to a newspaper. The treating health authority obtained an injunction restraining any breach of confidentiality. The newspaper published certain material and threatened to publish more. The court fined the newspaper for contempt and granted a permanent injunction restraining any further disclosure. The court did so on the basis that failure to maintain confidentiality would discourage others from seeking treatment:

'On the one hand, there are public interests in having a free and an informed public debate; on the other, it is in the public interest that actual or potential AIDS sufferers should be able to resort to hospitals without fear of being revealed, that those owing duties of confidence in their employment should be loyal and should not disclose confidential matters and that, prima facie, no one should be allowed to use information extracted in breach of confidence from hospital records even if disclosure of the particular information may not give rise to immediately apparent harm.'

On occasion with a 'doctor patient', as with any other patient, a question may arise as to competing public interests in maintaining confidentiality and public safety. The National Counselling Service for Sick Doctors is a confidential service provided by the profession. It is sometimes invoked by the doctor himself and other times by colleagues concerned that a doctor is not taking appropriate measures to deal with his/her health problems. Help comes from a doctor from outside the area concerned. Other groups exist to help doctors with health problems; notably the Doctors and Dentists Group, which helps with recovery from alcohol abuse.

Where a doctor is suffering from an infectious disease, that doctor is under a general ethical duty to consider the safety of his/her patients. The GMC has produced specific guidance with respect to doctors who consider that they may be suffering from HIV infection, requiring them to be tested and, if infected, to have regular medical supervision and seek and adhere to appropriate expert professional advice on any changes or restriction in their practice. Any doctor who is aware that counselling s/he has given with respect to professional activity in this context is not being followed is under a duty to take steps to warn an appropriate body, such as the GMC. Guidelines have now been introduced with respect to hepatitis B infection and immunisation. Where an individual is E-antigen positive, s/he is under a clear obligation not to carry out certain procedures.

Failure to take advice and modify practice is a criminal offence of committing a public nuisance, and may lead to imprisonment.

CASE STUDY 2 - REGINA V GAUD

Dr Gaud was a surgeon who became aware that he was E-antigen positive. Despite this he continued to assist in major surgery in a sequence of London Hospitals for a period of several years. On occasions when he was tested for hepatitis B, he substituted a sample of patient's blood for his own. After several moves of hospital, it was finally established that he was responsible for a number of cases of hepatitis B in surgical patients. At his trial at Southwark Crown Court in 1994, he pleaded guilty to committing a public nuisance and was sentenced to one year's imprisonment.

An FHSA has the power to take over the running of a GP's practice. This power may be exercised where there is real and substantial concern as to the fitness of a GP to provide general medical services to his/her patients.

The GMC has the power, under its health procedures, to take steps with respect to sick doctors. Section 37 of the *Medical Act* 1983 provides that where the fitness to practise of a fully registered person is judged by the Health Committee to be seriously impaired by reason of his/her physical or mental condition, the Committee may suspend registration for up to a year or impose conditions on it which they consider necessary for the protection of members of the public or in the interests of the doctor. The Preliminary Proceedings Committee can, in appropriate cases in order to protect the public, make an interim order suspending or imposing conditions on a doctor's practice. A doctor has a right to be heard before such decisions, by either Committee, are made. While Health Committee determinations may be appealed on a point of law to the Privy Council, in practice the findings of the Committee are unlikely to be overturned. Since the powers of the GMC Committees in health cases do not allow it to erase a doctor from the register, some doctors are reviewed by the Health Committee on an annual basis.

Nurses

The *Nurses, Midwives and Health Visitors Act* 1979 and the *Nurses, Midwives and Health Visitors (Professional Conduct) Rules* 1987 provide for the regulation of the nursing profession and are, in general terms, of similar effect to the *Medical Act*. A person may be removed from the register if *'she has been guilty of misconduct'* which includes convictions for criminal offences. Where a nurse has been convicted it is not open to the nurse to try to re-open the question of guilt; however, the fact of a conviction is not in itself determinative of the issue of misconduct. A conviction does not include a sentence of probation or a conditional or unconditional discharge. A nurse may also be removed from the register if *'her fitness to practice is seriously impaired by reason of her physical or mental condition'*. Unlike with doctors, this is an actual removal from the register rather than simply a suspension. A nurse may apply to be re-admitted to the register when s/he has been removed, whether for misconduct or ill-health.

Chapter 3

CONFIDENTIALITY, CONSENT AND PATIENT RECORDS

CONFIDENTIALITY

The confidentiality of the relationship between the patient and the doctor is fundamental to medical practice. The law recognises this, and that there is a public interest in maintaining that confidence. A doctor and his/her staff are therefore obliged to ensure that the information is not disclosed to anyone, and they may not use the information for their own benefits.

In very restricted circumstances, the communication of confidential information that an individual has may not be a breach of confidentiality. The duty does not apply to useless information or trivia (see Case Study 3), where the information is already generally publicly known; nor where there is a clear public interest that the information shall be disclosed. A doctor will always think carefully before disclosing information about a patient, and will handle the information so that only those who **need to know** will be informed. He or she will be careful to restrict information given to others (see Case Study 4).

CASE STUDY 3 - TRIVIAL?

Mrs A (the practice receptionist) telephoned a patient's home and, as the patient was out, left a message with her husband that the patient was to call at the surgery and pick up her test results. Mrs A was dismissed, and applied to the Industrial Tribunal claiming the dismissal was unfair.

'If the matter were looked at superficially, it would appear that dismissal for what might be described as a relatively trivial breach of confidentiality might not be regarded as a reasonable penalty. On the other hand, the Tribunal was satisfied, both from the evidence given and from their own experience, that confidentiality is of the essence in any medical practice and that any breach of confidentiality is not only most upsetting for the patient involved, but can have a devastating effect on a medical practice. The Tribunal is therefore of the view that even the slightest breach of confidentiality must be regarded by a reasonable employer in a medical practice most seriously, and that dismissal in such circumstances is appropriate. The Tribunal is therefore satisfied that despite the Applicant's long record of service with the Respondents, the Respondents did not act unreasonably in dismissing the Applicant for that reason and the application must be dismissed.'

(Industrial Tribunal decision from the records of the BMA)

CASE STUDY 4 - HOW NOT TO TALK TO PATIENTS

Patient A was sitting in the doctor's waiting room. Mrs B, the receptionist, came in and said: "Well who's been a silly girl then? How many weeks are you?". The patient was very distressed and left at once, angry. Mrs B told the doctor that she had whispered her comments, and she was reprimanded. A few days later in the school playground, a mother who had been in the waiting room at the time approached patient A and asked some personal questions. Patient A complained and Mrs B was dismissed.

'Even at the Tribunal Mrs B did not appear to appreciate the very serious breach of confidentiality which she had created. It was her contention, which the Tribunal did not believe, that she had no training in all her years of service. She did realise her remarks were unprofessional and she was also familiar with normal protocol. Answering a question from one of the members (of the Tribunal), she agreed that it might be a risk unacceptable to the doctors to continue her in her job.

Doctors receive sensitive information in confidence from patients and patients are reliant on confidentiality being maintained. Staff must observe confidentiality when handling patients' notes and transferring information. Should it become known that there are breaches of confidentiality, the public will cease to trust that practice, their confidence having been eroded. The General Medical Council may become involved, on the doctrine of vicarious liability a doctor may be censured or even erased from the register.'

The dismissal was upheld.

(Industrial Tribunal decision from the records of the BMA)

From time to time, a doctor will have to disclose information about a patient without the consent of the patient (Table 3). The GMC has advised that:

'A doctor who decides to disclose confidential information about an individual must be prepared to explain and justify that decision whatever the circumstances of the disclosure. . . Doctors who are faced with a difficult decision whether to disclose information without a patient's consent must weigh up carefully the argument for and against disclosure. If in doubt they would be wise to discuss the matter with an experienced colleague or to seek advice from a Medical Defence Society or professional association.'

TABLE 3. CIRCUMSTANCES WHERE DISCLOSURE OF INFORMATION IS PERMISSIBLE.

- Where the patient consents.
- In compliance with an order of the court.
- In discharge of a statutory duty, e.g. to report notifiable diseases etc.
- A disclosure to a family or to third parties in the interests of a patient.
- Disclosure in the public interest.
- Communications with other health professionals for the purposes of treatment.
- Disclosure for teaching and research purposes.

CONSENT

No adult may be given medical treatment without consent. To do so, even with the best of intentions, may constitute an assault on the patient for which the practitioner may incur civil liability to pay compensation or which may amount to a criminal offence. The more common problem, however, is not that the patient has been treated without consent, but that the patient and doctor have not communicated properly. It is becoming increasingly clear in case law that in many circumstances doctors may be held negligent if they have not properly explained the nature of any proposed treatment. In the context of a claim for compensation as a result of unsatisfactory treatment, consent means more than the doctor obtaining the patient's permission to give treatment. The principle of autonomy (mentioned above) is being increasingly enforced in civil courts in claims that a doctor has been professionally negligent where a doctor has not pointed out to the patient some of the possible risks and problems associated with treatment.

There are certain very limited circumstances in which adults may be treated without their consent. The most important of these are where a patient is so mentally ill or disordered that s/he is compulsorily admitted to hospital in his his/her own best interest under the provisions of the *Mental Health Act* 1983, and where the patient is unconscious and needs treatment as an emergency.

CHILDREN

For the purposes of medical treatment, all young people over the age of 16 can give valid consent to treatment and choose their own doctor without consulting their parents. In practice, many doctors consider it prudent to involve parents in decisions with respect to treatment up to the age of 18. If a person is under the age of 18, then the parent can consent to medical treatment on his/her behalf.

The respective rights of parents and children have been the subject of much anxious consideration by the courts. It has been held that: *'parental rights clearly do exist and they do not wholly disappear with the age of majority. . . Parental rights exist only so long as they are needed for the protection of the person and property of the child. . . Parental rights yield to the child's right to make his own decisions when he reaches a sufficient understanding and intelligence to be capable of making up his own mind on the matter requiring decision'*. In these circumstances, the individual child can make a decision, even if the child is under the age of 16.

Circumstances may arise where a child under the age of 16 does not want to involve parents in decision making concerning health care. This is most likely to arise in the case of a girl who does not wish her parents to know about her contraception. Following the decision in the Gillick case (on the subject of under-age girls receiving contraceptive advice from doctors), it is clear that in some circumstances a doctor can advise, prescribe and treat such a patient without notifying the parents, even though it is illegal for sexual intercourse to occur (Figure 5).

FIGURE 5 - CONFIDENTIALITY AND CONTRACEPTION UNDER THE AGE OF 16

Doctors should consider the following when consulted:

- Whether the patient understands the potential risks and benefits of the treatment and the advice given.

- The value of parental support must be discussed, and doctors must encourage young people to inform parents of the consultation and should discuss with the patient their reasons for not wishing to do so. It is important for persons under 16 seeking contraceptive advice to be aware that, although the doctor is legally obliged to discuss the value of parental support, the doctor will respect their confidentiality.

- The doctor should take into account whether the patient is likely to have sexual intercourse without contraception.

- The doctor should assess whether the patient's physical or mental health or both are likely to suffer if the patient does not receive contraceptive advice or supplies.

- The doctor must consider whether the patient's best interests would require the provision of contraceptive advice or methods or both without parental consent.

(Extract from guidance issued by BMA, GMSC, HEA, Brook Advisory Centres, FPA and RCGP)

Clearly, parents are the natural protectors of children, and a doctor will normally provide care and advice to children in conjunction with, and with the consent of, the parents. There are, however, circumstances where the interests of the parent and the child diverge. The doctor's primary responsibility is to the child and not to the parents. In extreme circumstances (such as child abuse cases) a doctor may be obliged to disclose information about the child without the consent of, or even without notifying, the parent.

MEDICAL RECORDS

At the heart of general practice are the medical records of patients. Because general practitioners take on responsibility for patients indefinitely (unlike hospital doctors who are normally only treating a patient for a specific illness), over time a GP will build up a detailed clinical history of the patient. This will contain information about illness and treatment, and it may also contain more general information about the patient or his/her family. Under GPs' *Terms of Service*, they are obliged to keep proper medical records on the forms provided by the FHSA, and these forms remain the property of the FHSA. A doctor owns the copyright in the record, and it is held under an obligation of confidentiality to the patient. It is clear, therefore, that many different people have an interest and stake in the medical records. Where a patient changes doctor, it is important that the doctor forwards the records as soon as possible to the FHSA for onward transmission to the next GP. The FHSA charter standards state:

> 'FHSAs should transfer records which are required urgently by doctors within two working days and they should complete routine transfer of records within 6 weeks.'

Although the patient is entitled to protection of the confidential information, until 1 November 1991 patients were not, as of right, entitled to inspect their own medical records. Then, under the provisions of the *Access to Health Records Act* 1990, patients became entitled to access to their own records. The definition of record is wide, and includes both the doctor's notes and those of the nurse and health visitor of that individual. A *'child patient'* is entitled to access providing the holder of the record (the GP) is satisfied that *'the patient is capable of understanding the nature of the application'*. Conversely, a parent shall not be given access unless the GP is satisfied that the child has consented or *'is incapable of understanding the nature of the application and the giving of access would be in his best interests'*.

The people who can apply for access to the record are the patient, a person with written authority applying on behalf of the patient, a person having parental responsibility for a 'child patient', a person appointed by a court to manage the affairs of an incompetent person and *'where the patient has died, the patient's personal representative and any person who may have a claim arising out of the patient's death'*. Clearly, this may in some circumstances create problems, and a further provision dealing with the position after the death of the patient states that *'when an application for access is made after the patient's death, access shall not be granted if the record includes a note, made at the patient's request, that he did not wish access to be given on such an application'* (see Figure 6).

FIGURE 6 - DENIAL OF ACCESS

- No access to a record dated prior to 1 November 1991, except to explain entries after 1 November 1991.

- No access to information where the information could cause serious harm to the physical or mental health of the patient or any other individual.

- No access which would give information relating to or provided by an individual other than the patient who could be identified from that individual unless the individual concerned has consented or the individual is a health professional involved in the care of the patient.

- Except where the application is directly approved by the patient, access shall not be given to any part of the record which in the opinion of the holder of the record would disclose information provided by the patient or obtained as a result of an examination or investigation to which the patient consented in the expectation that the information would not be disclosed.

- Where the patient has died access shall not be given to any part of the record which, in the opinion of the holder of the record, would disclose information which is not relevant to any claim which may arise out of the patient's death.

(From Section 5 of the Access to Health Records Act 1990)

Where information is held about an individual on computer, then, under the *Data Protection Act* 1984, that individual will usually have the right to access to the information. Under the *Access to Medical Reports Act* 1988, an individual is allowed to access to a medical report prepared for employment or insurance purposes. This report must have been prepared on his/her physical or mental health by a medical practitioner who is or has been responsible for the clinical care of the individual.

DATA PROTECTION

The *Data Protection Act* gives individuals rights with respect to the collection, use and communication of personal information about them which is held or processed on computer. The individual has rights of access to data about himself, can apply for rectification or erasure of inaccurate data, and is entitled to compensation for distress and harm caused by loss or disclosure of data or harm caused by inaccuracies. The access rights, with respect to health records, are in line with the general access rights considered above. The statute contains eight

TABLE 4. THE EIGHT DATA PROTECTION PRINCIPLES.

Broadly, these state that personal data must be:

1. Obtained and processed fairly and lawfully.

2. Held only for the lawful purposes described in the data user's entry.

3. Used only for the described purposes, and disclosed only to those people described in the register entry.

4. Adequate, relevant and not excessive in relation to the purpose for which it is held.

5. Accurate and, where necessary, kept up-to-date.

6. Held no longer than is necessary for the registered purpose.

7. Accessible to the individual concerned who, where appropriate, has the right to have information about him/herself corrected or erased.

8. Surrounded by proper security.

data protection principles, which guide holders of data and may determine the lawfulness of any particular use of data (Table 4).

The Data Protection Registrar is a public officer charged with ensuring adherence with the law and has published codes on various aspects of data protection. The GMSC has issued a code of practice on the Act as it affects GPs. This should be taken into account by GPs in setting their own local procedures for ensuring compliance with the law; the statutory provisions and guidance set out a system of good practice concordant with the ethical obligations of doctors. Most importantly, GPs should ensure that they are properly registered under the Act for all the data they have and for all its uses.

MENTAL HEALTH

As part of the modern reaction to the ethical outrages committed by doctors under the Nazi regime, there has been increasing focus on the need for patients' consent before treatment is attempted. From the 1960s onwards it became increasingly clear that in Soviet institutions, some doctors were identifying as psychiatric illness patterns of behaviour and systems of belief which, in liberal democracies, are perceived as proper and praiseworthy. The law relating to mental health in the UK is an attempt to structure the treatment of mentally ill patients which, in a highly contentious area, provides ethically acceptable responses to the questions of consent and the diagnosis of illness which inspire public confidence, respect the rights of patients and are clinically meaningful. The *Mental Health Act* 1983 was the result of long and detailed consultation and discussion, with the Department of Health struggling to find a structure which was acceptable to all the many interested parties, most notably psychiatrists and groups concerned with the civil liberties of patients. One of the key provisions of the Act is the right of appeal to the Mental Health Review Tribunal which has oversight of the use of the compulsory powers contained in the Act. Many thousands of such appeals are made each year.

The Act deals with questions as to the care and treatment of mentally disordered patients and also deals with problems in the management of their property. For the purposes of this book, only issues with compulsory admission to hospital under Part II of the Act where GPs are likely to be involved will be discussed. The Act defines 'mental disorder' as:

> *'mental illness, arrested or incomplete development of mind, psychopathic disorder or disability of mind'*
> (from Section 1(2) *Mental Health Act*)

The Act is careful, in the light of prevailing social values, to restrict the ambit of the definition:

> *'Nothing in subsection (2) above shall be construed as implying that a person may be dealt with under this Act as suffering from mental disorder, or from any form of mental disorder described in this section, by reason only of promiscuity or other immoral conduct, sexual deviancy or dependence on alcohol or drugs'*

Section 2 provides that a patient may be compulsorily admitted and detained for assessment for a period of up to 28 days on the certificate of two medical practitioners that s/he is suffering from mental disorder of a nature, or to a degree, which warrants detention in hospital for assessment, or assessment followed by treatment for a period of time, and the detention is necessary in the interests of the patient's health and safety or in order to protect others. Admissions under this provision are initiated by the nearest relative or an approved social worker. A patient may be discharged early by the responsible medical officer, the hospital managers or the nearest relative (the RMO can prohibit a relative-initiated discharge). In addition, Section 4 contains emergency powers for compulsory admission for assessment on the same grounds for up to 72 hours where one doctor (usually the GP) supports an application by the nearest relative or approved social worker for an admission for assessment where the delay in obtaining the opinion of a second doctor would cause undesirable delay.

Section 3 provides for compulsory admission for treatment for a period of up to six months, which may be renewed. Here, the application must be supported by a recommendation by two medical practitioners (one 'approved' by the Secretary of State as having special experience in the treatment or diagnosis of mental illness), stating that:

- the patient is suffering from mental illness, severe mental impairment or psychopathic disorder, or that mental disorder is of a nature or degree which makes it appropriate for him/her to receive medical treatment in a hospital;

- in the case of psychopathic disorder or mental impairment, such treatment is likely to alleviate or prevent a deterioration of his/her condition; and

- it is necessary for the health and safety of the patient or for the protection of other persons that s/he should receive such treatment, and it cannot be provided unless s/he is detained under the Section.

A magistrate has power, on the application of an approved social worker, to grant the police a warrant to enter premises and remove a person believed to be suffering from mental disorder who has been, or is being, ill-treated, neglected or kept under improper control, or is unable to care for him/herself if living alone. When the police execute the warrant they need to be accompanied by an approved social worker and a registered medical practitioner.

Chapter 4

MEDICAL NEGLIGENCE

In ordinary civil law, compensation can be claimed by one individual against another if they have been injured by that other person's negligence. In order to establish a right to compensation, an individual will need to establish that:

- the other person owed him/her a duty of care;
- s/he was in breach of that duty; and
- harm was caused to him/her by that breach of duty - i.e. by that carelessness.

Although the rules are themselves easy to state, the working out of those rules against the factual background of contemporary clinical practice is a matter of considerable complexity.

In medical cases, there is normally no question as to whether or not a duty of care exists. For a general practitioner, the question normally resolves itself to one of determining whether or not a patient comes within the *Terms of Service* definitions of a GP's patient. Where a doctor is treating a patient, or is under an obligation to treat the patient (e.g. by visiting), then the doctor owes to that patient a duty of care.

Extent of the duty of care

In the leading case on medical negligence, Bolam v Friern Hospital Management Committee, the Judge held that:

*'The test is the standard of the **ordinary** skilled man exercising and professing to have that special skill. **A** man need not possess the highest expert skills; it is well established law that it is sufficient if he exercises the ordinary skill of an ordinary competent man exercising that particular art.'*

It is here that the key distinction arises between general practice and hospital practice. A patient presenting him/herself at a doctor's surgery is entitled to a level of clinical competence in the care the doctor gives him/her consistent with the knowledge and experience of a skilled GP. The standard of care does not vary according to whether the doctor entered into general practice yesterday or 20 years ago. Where the practitioner is providing services, such as minor surgery, then the standard of care is that which may be reasonably expected of a GP providing minor surgery.

If that same general practitioner works as a clinical assistant in a district general hospital performing the same minor surgery, then the duty of care is to be assessed as against the standard that should be expected of an individual holding that post (Wilsher v Essex AHA). However, in the hospital context, different questions could arise because of differences with respect to the availability of specialist advice or services. In medical indemnity terms, however, in the former case the GP will be responsible for the damage caused, but in the latter liability will be with the hospital under the arrangements with respect to medical indemnity which were brought into effect in 1990. In Whitehouse v Jordan, Lord Donaldson summarised the position:

> 'If a doctor fails to exercise the skill which he has or claims to have he is in breach of his duty of care. He is negligent.'

The standard of care

In many cases there will be some doubt as to what is the appropriate medical treatment or investigation. In Bolam it was held that a doctor who acted:

> 'in accordance with the practice accepted as proper by a responsible body of medical men skilled in that particular area . . . [a doctor is not guilty of negligence] if he is acting in accordance with such a practice, merely because there is a body of opinion which would take a contrary view.'

In determining whether there has been negligence, therefore, a key question to be established is whether or not treatment has been in accordance with accepted professional practice. While this is a test applied in all cases relating to crafts and professions, it is always open to a Judge to challenge the accepted practice as unsatisfactory because it fails to take proper account of the risks and benefits involved in the procedure.

In Sidaway, the Court of Appeal suggested that in certain circumstances the Courts might intervene and the court should properly address the question of whether a practice was 'accepted as proper by a body of skilled and experienced medical men'. Overall, however, the Courts are most reluctant to intervene in a way which suggests that they are rejecting the weight of informed medical opinion on a clinical matter.

In order to be protected and to demonstrate that the practice which s/he followed is acceptable to an informed body of medical opinion, it is necessary for a GP to ensure that s/he is reasonably up to date, i.e. that s/he is adopting current practice. Clearly this is most simply done by reading journals and going on courses. No general practitioner would be expected to be fully aware of all the potentially relevant clinical developments. Doctors should ensure that they are constantly learning and (where appropriate) modifying their practice in the light of this new information. In one decided case, it was held that failure to read one article did not amount to negligence. However, from 1995, any general practitioner who fails to take the publicly recommended precautions with respect to hepatitis B, will clearly be negligent, even though s/he might not have been so acting the same way five or 10 years before. While a practitioner may be allowed a reasonable time to come to terms with new developments, this is limited.

CONSEQUENTIAL DAMAGE

One of the great areas of difficulty in medical negligence cases, unlike (for example) motor injury cases, is establishing that the proven negligence of the doctor caused harm to the patient. In certain cases, it may be demonstrated that the clinical failures had no significant impact on the outcome. In many cases, the condition after treatment is simply the result of the development of the pre-existing condition. The issue has to be demonstrated by the plaintiff on a balance of probabilities. In Hotson, the court determined that there was a 25% chance that the misdiagnosis had affected the outcome significantly, thus the plaintiff failed in the action. Where there are many causes then the plaintiff needs to demonstrate that, on balance, the negligence materially contributed to the harm suffered. Another hurdle which plaintiffs may have to surmount is establishing that the loss or injury was foreseeable and not too remote. In Prendergast (see below), it was held that the GP was liable for the brain damage caused by the pharmacist misreading a prescription.

Burden of proof

In cases of negligence it is up to the plaintiff to demonstrate, on the balance of probabilities, every element necessary to establish the defendant's liability. This is so even where a new and innovative or unorthodox treatment is used (Wilsher v Essex AHA). In certain circumstances, however, a plaintiff may plead *res ipsa loquitur* - the matter speaks for itself. Its usefulness is in circumstances where the plaintiff is unable to specify exactly what caused the injury. In Cassidy v Ministry of Health, Lord Denning stated:

> 'If the plaintiff had to prove that some particular doctor or nurse was negligent, he would not be able to do it. But he was not put to that impossible task. He says, "I went into the hospital to be cured of two stiff fingers. I have come out with four stiff fingers, and my hand is useless. That should not have happened if due care had been used. Explain it, if you can." I am quite clearly of the opinion that raises a prima facie case against the hospital authorities. They have in no way explained how it could happen without negligence. They have busied themselves in saying that this or that member of staff was not negligent. But they have called not a single person to say that the injuries were consistent with due care on the part of all the members of the staff'.

Once the principle is established, the burden falls on the defendant to show that there is a credible alternative explanation which does not involve his/her negligence. If s/he is unable to do so then liability attaches to him/her.

Compensation

Where an individual is injured through another's tort, the law provides for financial compensation. The court endeavours to put the injured individual in the position s/he would have been in had the injury not occurred. The sums awarded cover aspects of both financial loss (both before trial and reasonably anticipated in the future) and non-pecuniary loss. The latter is compensation to the plaintiff for the pain and suffering and loss of physical amenity (e.g. loss of the ability to enjoy a game of golf etc.) which is the result of the injury. In one leading case Lord Diplock observed:

> 'Any figure at which the assessment of damages arrives cannot be other than artificial and, if the aim is that justice meted out to all litigants should be even-handed instead of depending on the idiosyncrasies of the assessor, whether jury or judge, the figure must be basically a conventional figure derived from experience and from awards in comparable cases.'

Since personal injury cases are tried by a judge sitting alone, and there are published guidelines, the compensation for pain and suffering is relatively easy to calculate. The sums involved are surprisingly small when compared with damages awards sometimes made in actions for defamation, where the damages are assessed by juries in a less structured way. The financial loss calculation, where there is any continuing disability, may be complex and involve not merely loss of income, but many related questions such as the need for nursing care. It is now possible for the courts to award provisional damages in circumstances where the course of disease is uncertain, thus enabling the plaintiff to return to court in the event of a serious deterioration in his/her condition.

Where the plaintiff dies before the case comes to trial, the course of action continues for the benefit of his/her estate; although clearly the various calculations of loss will be on a different basis.

COMMON AREAS OF NEGLIGENCE CLAIMS

The key areas of responsibility with respect to patients which are identified in GPs' *Terms of Service* are reflected in the pattern of negligence claims against general practitioners. Some 20-25% of service committee hearings against GPs relate to a failure to visit. These cases can, in certain circumstances, give rise to claims of negligence where, for example, treatment for meningitis is delayed.

Failures of communication

Many problems arise through inadequate communication of clinically significant matters between GP, GP staff, hospital and patient. If the court considers that the failure is by the GP or his/her staff, then liability will fall on him.

In Lobley v Going, a child plaintiff with respiratory difficulties was kept waiting to see a GP for 15 minutes despite the father having told the receptionist: "He has got worse, he is having a bit of difficulty with his breathing". The Court of Appeal held that the receptionist had not been clearly told that this was an emergency, accordingly she had not been negligent.

In Coles v Reading and District Hospital Management Committee, Mr Coles, who had crushed his finger, saw his GP after attending at a cottage hospital where he was told to go to the general hospital. The GP failed to enquire properly of the patient as to what advice he had received and simply changed the dressing. The patient developed tetanus and the court held that the GP was negligent in not making proper inquiries.

In other cases, a failure to take a proper history and a hasty misdiagnosis which could have been avoided if the doctor had listened to the patient, founded successful claims in negligence. Other key areas of difficulty are failure to consider test results and failure to ensure that they are properly acted upon.

Misdiagnosis

Diagnosis is fundamental to the practice of medicine and it is unsurprising that failures of diagnosis, particularly in children, have given rise to a body of claims against GPs. In Sa'd v Robinson and Dunlop, GPs were held to be liable for failing to identify damage to a toddler's oesophagus following an incident with a teapot. They were also at fault in failing to examine fully, and in not referring quickly, and with appropriate information, to a hospital.

Referrals should contain sufficient information about the patient's condition and other relevant information to ensure that the hospital is apprised of all relevant factors within the GP's knowledge - including the urgency of the condition.

Prescription

Another significant category relates to the failure to prescribe appropriately, for example as a result of not establishing the existence of a known sensitivity to a drug. Doctors have been held liable for a pharmacist's misdispensing when the handwriting was unclear (Prendergast v Sam and Dee Limited). Difficulties can also arise with repeat prescriptions, especially of drugs which may be open to abuse.

Consent

While the issue of consent is considered elsewhere in this volume (Chapter 3), in the context of medical ethics and mental health, it also has direct implications for the lawfulness of medical interventions. In order for consent by a patient to be effective it must be voluntary, competent and adequately informed. However, these three criteria are not totally independent and they need to be considered in the light of the circumstances of the case. Issues of competency arise with respect to children and those lacking mental capacity; the degree of competence needed will vary according to the gravity of any proposed treatment. There has been discussion of the extent to which consent is voluntary when it is inadequately informed. If the patient is informed in broad terms of the nature of any procedure and then gives consent, the consent is voluntary. If such consent is not obtained, then the tort of battery has been committed. Where such consent has been obtained, then a doctor could be liable in negligence purely for a failure to explain the consequences and hazards of a procedure in accordance with accepted medical practice (i.e. the Bolam test). The fact that consent has been obtained should be recorded in the notes, together with a summary of any issues raised by the patient and any information given by the GP.

PRODUCT LIABILITY

One significant area of development in recent years has been the introduction of the 'general safety requirement' with respect to manufactured goods. This covers many products supplied, used or prescribed by GPs, from steroids to sterilisers and sutures. This legislation has its origins in the desire of the European Union to ease trade between member states by ensuring that there is a common basis for liability in respect of defective goods traded in the community. The Product Liability Directive (enacted in the UK as Part I of the *Consumer Protection Act* 1987) introduces the concept of strict liability on the manufacturer with respect to harm caused by his products. This clearly has great significance for pharmaceutical manufacturers and others supplying materials used in clinical practice.

A product is defective if the safety of the product is not as people are entitled to expect. In determining what it is reasonable to expect, all the circumstances are to be taken into account, including:

- The manner in which, and purposes for which, the product has been marketed, its get up, the use of any mark in relation to the product, any instructions for, or warnings with respect to, doing or refraining from doing anything with, or in relation to, the product.
- What might reasonably be expected to be done with, or in relation to, the product.
- The time when the product was supplied by its producer to another.

For GPs, the key issues therefore are ensuring that in supplying anything to a patient they are doing so in accordance with the manufacturer's guidelines and also ensuring that they keep records of the source of materials supplied. In order to ensure that they can identify the supplier in any litigation, doctors should retain supply records for at least 11 years. If a GP is unable to identify the source of defective material (e.g. a suture) then s/he will stand in the shoes of the manufacturer. In any litigation, the plaintiff will still have to demonstrate that the defective product actually caused the harm complained of. As yet this legislation has not been extensively tested in the courts, but it has caused some concern among manufacturers. Concern has been expressed that if a single-use product is re-used then the liability for any defect passes to the doctor. It may also attract criminal liability for supplying a device which does not comply with the *Medical Devices Regulations* 1994.

INCIDENCE OF CLAIMS

There has been a substantial increase in the incidence of claims of medical negligence. Although there are no comprehensive figures available, partial figures released by the Department of Health indicate that in excess of £50,000,000 compensation was paid out in 1992. It is believed that the great majority of cases of medical negligence are brought with the assistance of the legal aid fund. Legal aid figures for England and Wales (1987/8) indicate that 4,761 certificates were issued to assist plaintiffs bringing such claims; in 1993/4 that figure had risen to 10,857, which amounted to 5.7% of all legal aid certificates and 37.4% of certificates issued for personal injury claims. However, the incidence of success for plaintiffs in medical negligence litigation is substantially lower than that for other personal injury claims; the ratio of legal costs to damages recovered is also substantially higher.

There are relatively few reported cases of claims of medical negligence against general practitioners. This is clearly for a variety of reasons; however, the following may be significant:

- The general practitioner tends to have a long-term relationship with the patient; as a family friend s/he is less likely to receive a complaint.
- The complaints procedure to the FHSA provides a means for patients to raise their concerns.
- The system of referral from GP to NHS hospital specialist; moving the focus of care in difficult or acute cases may enable patients to shift the focus of their concern about medical treatment to the hospital.
- A patient attending at a doctor's surgery sees a specialist general practitioner providing services. A patient attending at a hospital, while under the care of a consultant, may well be seen and treated primarily by junior doctors in training who are not specialists.

Limitation

The general rule is that proceedings for personal injury must be launched within three years of the cause of action accruing: that is three years after the plaintiff discovers that s/he has suffered injury. Although problems can arise where the injury progresses from some minor harm, the rule here is that anything other than trivial harm starts the clock running. In order for time to run, the plaintiff must know:

- the identity of the defendant,
- that the injury is significant, and
- that the harm is attributable in whole or part to the negligent act or omission.

The law allows an extension of time where the plaintiff is under a disability at the time of the injury, i.e. under 18 or a person of unsound mind who is incapable of managing his/her affairs by reason of mental disorder within the *Mental Health Act*. In such cases, time does not start to run until the individual ceases to be under a disability or dies. If the defendant improperly conceals the facts of the case then this will postpone the running of time until the plaintiff ought to have discovered this. The court may disapply the time limits where, in the light of all the circumstances, it is just to do so.

Medical records

In any negligence proceedings, medical records are the crucial evidence. It is therefore essential that they are adequate, and also that they are available for use in any subsequent litigation. Given the uncertainties of the limitation period, the length of time they should be retained is clearly problematic. A GP is, under the *Terms of Service*, obliged to keep records and return them to the FHSA on the death or de-registration of the patient. However, a GP may also have private patients whose records s/he will retain. Department of Health guidance to health authorities recommends that:

- Obstetric records should be retained for 25 years.
- Records relating to persons under the age of 18 should be retained until age 25, or eight years after the last entry.
- Records of mentally disordered persons should be retained for 20 years after no further care is necessary.
- All other personal health records should be retained for eight years after the conclusion of the treatment.

Where the patient has died, the minimum retention period is eight years, except for obstetric records - where more than one life is involved.

Wrongful life

Lawyers are constantly seeking new ways of helping their clients obtain redress. One recent innovation is the claim for wrongful life. These claims are based on the case that the child would not have been born but for an act of medical negligence. This may take many forms, ranging from a failure to advise properly about the risks of a sterilisation to the failure of antenatal diagnosis of disability. The extent to which there may be a right to compensation will vary considerably; however, the Court of Appeal has indicated that damages may be awarded for such matters as the mother's pain and suffering of pregnancy and childbirth, and the financial costs of bringing up the child.

Chapter 5

EMPLOYMENT LAW

Thirty years ago, employment law was a very minor branch of the law of contract, hardly earning more than a few pages in any legal text book. Since then, however, there has been an explosion of legislation in the UK Parliament, which has set out a new scheme of rights and responsibilities for employers and employees, a new system of courts (the Industrial Tribunals and the Employment Appeal Tribunal) to consider cases, and a substantial amount of European law revising these rights. This legislation has been the subject of interpretation in many thousands of cases before the tribunals and courts. The result is that, in a relatively short space of time, a body of law many thousands of pages long has been generated.

The effect of all these changes has been that the law now recognises that employment gives a status and responsibility to the employee, and that 19th century 'hire and fire' attitudes are out of date in modern society.

Employers normally require references before they employ a worker. With young workers this is likely to be a school or college reference; after that it is normal to rely on a reference from the current or previous employer. The employer is not obliged to issue a reference; however, any reference given should be accurate and state facts correctly. The previous employer owes the employee a duty to take reasonable care as to the accuracy of facts contained in the reference.

Employees now have the right to a written statement of their terms of employment (Table 5), an itemised pay statement, protection from unfair dismissal, rights to redundancy payment and the right not to be discriminated against on grounds of race, sex or trade union membership. These rights can be enforced by means of an application to the Industrial Tribunal.

If some of the details of the terms of employment with respect to sickness and pension arrangements are contained in a collective agreement, they do not need to be given to the employee providing the employee has a reasonable opportunity to see the agreement. However, the statement of the names of the parties, the start of employment, pay interval, hours of work, holiday pay, place of work and job title and description have to be included in one document.

Where any of the terms of employment are changed, an employer has to give notice of the change to the employee within one month (this enables the employee to object to any such changes at an early stage). Where a contract is in operation, it is not usually possible to change the contract without the consent of both parties to it, although a written contract may contain arrangements which allow for changes in matters of pay, place of work and other areas. Even then, if an employer tries to change the contract he or she must do so in a reasonable and fair way. If an employer changes a contract without the consent of the employee, this is a breach of contract. If this is a substantial change, the employee may be able to claim compensation for unfair dismissal or redundancy. Clearly, if the change is only a minor one or is in the employee's benefit, it is unlikely that there will be any difficulty. An employer should seek agreement to any change of contract and give adequate notice of the change. If a dispute does arise, then an

TABLE 5. EMPLOYMENT PARTICULARS.

Within two months of the beginning of employment, an employee shall receive a statement (or statements) with the following information:

- Job title and job description.
- The names of the employer and the employee.
- The date the employment began.
- The date on which continuous employment began (where previous employment counts towards a period of employment).
- Pay rates.
- Whether pay is weekly or monthly.
- Terms and conditions relating to hours of work.
- Details of holiday and holiday pay.
- Arrangements for ill health, including any sick pay arrangements.
- Details of any pension or pension schemes.
- Notice periods for the employee and the employer.
- Whether the job is permanent and, if not, how long it will continue or the date of termination for a fixed-term contract.
- The place or places of work and the address of the employer.
- Particulars of any collective agreements directly affecting terms and conditions of employment and, where the employer is not a party, the identity of the persons who are parties to the agreement.

Industrial Tribunal will need to consider whether the change was a reasonable one in all the circumstances of the business.

For every employer who employs more than 20 employees, the statement given to employees must include a note specifying any disciplinary rules, or grievance and disciplinary procedures applying to the employment. It is good practice to do this even in the case of employers with fewer than 20 staff.

Every employee is entitled to have an itemised pay statement which indicates the gross pay, the amount of deductions and the purpose for which the money is taken (usually tax and national insurance) and the net amount of pay. If there is any dispute about whether the correct amount of money has been paid, then under the terms of the *Wages Act* 1986, an employee is entitled to apply to an Industrial Tribunal alleging an unauthorised deduction from pay. In addition, if there is uncertainty as to what the terms of a contract of employment are, an employee may apply to the Tribunal for a determination.

INDUSTRIAL TRIBUNALS

Industrial Tribunals were created nearly 25 years ago in recognition that employment law was a very different sort of code from the sorts of law then considered in County Courts, and that justice would benefit from the participation of people with direct experience of industry in the decision-making process. Accordingly, an Industrial Tribunal consists of three members: a legally qualified chairman and two individuals, one nominated by employers' associations and one by trade unions. The insight and experience of these individuals has been crucial in allowing Industrial Tribunals to reflect the realities of life rather than getting too caught up in legal theorising. Applications to an Industrial Tribunal must normally be made within three months of the event complained of (except for redundancy claims). However, in exceptional circumstances the time limit may be waived. Appeals from the Industrial Tribunals are the responsibility of the Employment Appeal Tribunal, which again consists of a lawyer (in this case a high court judge or another senior judge) and the nominees of the two sides of industry.

If a claim against unfair dismissal succeeds, an employee may be reinstated to his/her old job with continuous employment or re-engagement. However, tribunals award this in only a very small number of cases. Where this is awarded and the employer fails to implement it, then further compensation may be awarded. More usually, where a tribunal finds that an employee has been unfairly dismissed, the tribunal makes a financial award consisting of a basic award and a compensatory award. Both of these may be reduced in the light of the conduct of the employee. The basic award is calculated in terms of the length of service and the rate of pay. The compensatory award seeks to compensate the employee for the loss which the employee has suffered as a result of the dismissal. The average award is about £2,000, although awards of over £10,000 are possible. In claims relating to discrimination on the grounds of race or sex, compensation for the feelings of distress and humiliation is possible. In order to comply with European law, there is no maximum limit for awards relating to sex discrimination, and the provisions of the *Race Relations Act* have been amended to bring the two sets of rights into line. Other awards made by Industrial Tribunals are subject to statutory limits. Industrial Tribunals also have jurisdiction to determine breach of contract cases up to a value of £25,000.

DISCIPLINE AND DISMISSAL

The most important right given by the statutory framework of employment law is the right, under certain circumstances, to complain to an Industrial Tribunal against an unfair dismissal. *The Employment Protection (Consolidation) Act* 1978 defines dismissal as:

- Where the employer terminates the contract with or without notice.
- Where a contract for a fixed term is not renewed.

- Where the employee terminates the contract in circumstances where s/he has a right to do so because of the employer's conduct (constructive dismissal). In any case of constructive dismissal, it is for the tribunal to decide whether or not, on the facts, the employee was entitled to end the contract.

- The refusal to allow a woman to exercise her right to return to work after having her baby.

However, there is no right to apply to the Industrial Tribunal if the employee has less than two years' service (except in discrimination cases), or is over the normal retirement age of the business (if there is no normal retirement age, over 65).

The employer has to show the Industrial Tribunal that the principal reason for the dismissal was to justified, and:

- Was related to the capability or qualifications of the employee for doing his/her work.

- Was related to the conduct of the employee.

- That the employee was redundant.

- That the employment was unlawful.

- That there was some other substantial reason justifying dismissal.

Even where the employer has shown the above, the tribunal has to decide whether the dismissal was fair or unfair by considering whether the employer acted reasonably or unreasonably in treating it as a sufficient reason for dismissal in accordance with *equity and the substantial merits of the case*. This is the key issue in many hearings, and it is not a matter of whether the tribunal would have come to the same decision as the employer, but whether the employer's decision was reasonable, bearing in mind the size and administrative resources of the employer and the choices open to him.

Some of the key points which have emerged from cases include the fact that the employer has to follow a fair procedure. What a fair procedure is depends upon the circumstances of the case and the size of the employer. In a GP practice, where there is usually only a small group of staff and doctors, it is not usually possible to have a very complicated system for disciplinary hearings. In one decided case, it was held that: *we are satisfied that the respondents carried out a reasonable procedure although it is unfortunate that because of the size of this enterprise there could be no appeal*.

The Advisory Conciliation and Arbitration Service (ACAS) is a government agency responsible for assisting in the resolution of all sorts of disputes between employers and employees. Among other activities, it has published various codes and handbooks on matters affecting good practice in resolving disputes and handling disciplinary and other questions arising in employment.

Capability

In dealing with issues of incompetence, it is recognised that 'counselling' staff and giving them appropriate training is good practice. In competence cases, warnings prior to dismissal are usual. This lets employees know that their job is in peril, and helps them to focus on the areas of work that need improvement. Where a warning has been given, sufficient time must be allowed to the employee to bring his/her work up to standard.

Where the issue of capability is concerned with the employee's ill-health, an employer must be adequately informed of the medical position. The employer needs to consider how long they can get by without the employee, and whether any alternative arrangements can be made so that the employee can continue in work.

Conduct

Where an employee is dismissed for misconduct, a three-fold test has evolved to assist the tribunal in determining whether or not the dismissal is fair:

- Did the employer genuinely believe that the employee was guilty of misconduct?
- Was that belief reasonable?
- Did the employer investigate the matter reasonably?

REDUNDANCY AND TRANSFER OF STAFF

Where there is a change in the doctors running a partnership, although the employer has changed, the staff have continued their employment and there is no question of redundancy. The position is the same when a single-handed GP retires and the whole of his/her practice is taken on by another doctor. Where a GP's list is split between various practices, then a redundancy situation could arise. Redundancy arises either when the employer ceases carrying on the business, or when the employer's requirements for workers has ceased or diminished regardless of whether the amount of work required to be done remains the same. In such circumstances, employees who have been employed for more than two years are entitled to a redundancy payment.

An employer is obliged to consult any recognised trade unions in connection with redundancies. Furthermore, an employer is obliged to consider offering suitable alternative work to any potentially redundant employee, although the ability of a GP to find alternative work for staff is likely to be restricted. In selecting staff for redundancy, employers are under an obligation not to discriminate on the grounds of sex, race or trade union membership. UK law does not, at present, recognise discrimination on the grounds of age as a matter requiring legal remedies. Indeed, an employee is not entitled to claim unfair dismissal at all if s/he has attained the normal retirement age of 65, except in circumstances where one of the inadmissible reasons is the reason for dismissal (i.e. discrimination on the grounds of race, sex, trade union membership or health and safety activity).

DISCRIMINATION

The *Sex Discrimination Act* (SDA) and the *Race Relations Act* (RRA) require employers to act in way that is not discriminatory on the grounds of sex and marital status (SDA), or on the grounds of colour, race, nationality, citizenship, or ethnic or national origin (RRA).

These Acts require employers not to discriminate in their recruitment and selection procedures, or in the terms upon which they employ staff, or offer them training, pay or promotion, or in any other way treat a person less favourably on the grounds of race or sex than s/he would treat someone else. In addition to direct discrimination, indirect discrimination is also prohibited. This is where, while it would appear that treatment is fair, an unjustified condition or restriction effectively means that, in proportion, many more people are excluded on the grounds of their sex or race than other individuals. An example of this would be requiring job applicants to be over six foot tall - this would be indirectly discriminatory against women; or requiring them to have degrees from UK universities - this would discriminate against comparable applicants with degrees from universities overseas.

In selection for recruitment, it is wise to advertise the post and measure the applicants against clear, written and objective standards relevant to the actual performance of the job. An informal method of recruitment, for example word of mouth, leaves the employer open to a charge of discrimination which is harder to disprove; it also deprives the employer of the opportunity of assessing a wide range of possibly very good applicants.

PART-TIME STAFF

In general practice, the vast majority of staff are part-time. In UK Employment Law, part-time staff who worked fewer than 16 hours a week were disadvantaged compared with those who worked more. However, recent changes in UK law have given part-time staff equal rights with full-time employees.

MATERNITY

The *Trade Union Reform and Employment Rights Act* 1993 (TURERA) made significant changes to many aspects of the law relating to employment and pregnancy. This was to bring UK law into line with the extended rights granted under the European Union Directive on Pregnancy.

Where a woman is dismissed for pregnancy or a connected reason before the expected date of birth, the dismissal is automatically unfair unless at the date of dismissal it would be unlawful of the employer to continue to employ her or because she was incapable by reason of pregnancy of adequately doing the work for which she was employed. Such circumstances are unlikely to arise in general practice, and are more likely to affect those working with dangerous chemicals or X-ray equipment. Any reason connected with pregnancy is interpreted very broadly so that illness associated with, or related to, pregnancy falls within the definition. There is no qualifying period of employment for bringing a claim in these circumstances.

Under TURERA, an employee is entitled to at least 14 weeks' maternity leave irrespective of hours of work and length of service. In addition, where an employee has worked for more than two years, there is a separate statutory right to return to work after a period of absence on account of pregnancy and confinement. There is a complicated system of giving notice to ensure the preservation of these rights; these are linked to the entitlement to receive statutory maternity pay (SMP), which requires the individual to intend to return to work. However, even if a woman fails to comply with the deadlines, an Industrial Tribunal may hold that she still has the right to return to the job.

A pregnant worker has a right not to be unreasonably refused time off with pay during working hours in order to receive antenatal care. In order to have this right, she needs an appointment to receive care from the doctor, midwife or health visitor and, apart from her first appointment, she is obliged to produce, at the request of her employer, confirmation that she is pregnant and an appointment card.

In order to receive SMP, an employee must meet the following conditions:

- Be pregnant at the 11th week before her expected week of confinement, or have had the baby by that time.
- Be continuously employed for at least 26 weeks, ending with the week immediately preceding the 14th week before the expected week of confinement (the qualifying week).
- Have normal weekly earnings of sufficiently high level.
- Have stopped working for the employer.

SMP is available to the employee who is absent from work. Accordingly, it is necessary for there to be some continuing intention to return for SMP to be payable.

Maternity rights are perhaps the most complicated area in the whole of employment law. It is essential that any individual employee establishes her rights at as early a stage as is possible, and seeks appropriate advice in order to ensure that she receives SMP, and has a smooth return to work after confinement.

Chapter 6

HEALTH AND SAFETY

General practitioners employ staff and occupy premises. As such, they have responsibility for much that goes on at those premises. Some of these obligations have been evolved over the centuries by the common law, and require them not to be careless. This duty of care and the obligations in the tort of negligence were acknowledged to be inadequate even after the *Occupiers Liability Act* 1957 was passed. This stated that an occupier of premises owed a common duty of care to all his/her visitors. The common duty was defined as:

> 'A duty to take such care as in all the circumstances of the case is reasonable to see that the visitor will be reasonably safe in using the premises for the purpose for which he is invited or permitted by the occupier to be there.'

However, for almost two centuries, Parliament has repeatedly legislated to protect the well-being of employees in different industries. This culminated in the passing of the *Health and Safety at Work Act* 1974.

HEALTH & SAFETY AT WORK ACT 1974

This Act is designed to secure the health, safety and welfare of people at work. It also protects others against risks to health and safety arising from working practices and dangerous substances used or produced at work. The Act provides a general framework and ministers have, under the powers it contains, produced a large number of statutory instruments on different aspects of health and safety. The whole process has, in recent years, been influenced by the development of European law in this field.

The Health and Safety Executive (HSE) (a body set up under the Act) is responsible, together with local authorities, for enforcing the law. The Act provides that breach of the duties set out in the Act, or under the regulations, amounts to a criminal offence. In practice, the enforcement authorities are usually more concerned to ensure that the law is complied with, and that good practice is adopted, than to prosecute. However, they will prosecute in serious matters.

If an individual is in any way harmed by a breach of regulations made under the *Health and Safety at Work Act* (but not a breach of the Act itself) then s/he may be able to sue the employer and get compensation for the breach of statutory duty without worrying whether s/he would be compensated under the law of negligence or contract. Section 2 of the Act makes it the general duty of employers to ensure, so far as is reasonably practicable, the health, safety and welfare at work of all his/her employees (see Figure 7). It may well be harder for an employer to prove that something is not 'reasonably practicable' than it is to prove that s/he is not being negligent.

FIGURE 7 - SPECIFIC DUTIES OF EMPLOYERS TO EMPLOYEES

So far as reasonably practicable to:

- Provide and maintain plant and systems of work which are safe and without risk to health.

- Make arrangements to ensure safety and absence of risk to health in connection with the use, handling, storage and transport of articles and substances.

- Provide such information, instruction, training and supervision as is necessary to ensure health and safety at work for employees.

- Maintain any place of work under his/her control together with the means of access to the place of work in a safe state without risk to health.

- Provide a working environment for staff which is safe without risk to health and adequate as regards facilities and arrangements for welfare at work.

(From Section 2, Health & Safety at Work Act 1974)

The HSE appoints inspectors to visit businesses and ensure that statutory requirements are carried out. These inspectors have the right to come onto the premises without permission and, if they are investigating an incident, they can interview and take written statements from anybody with information. If they find something wrong, they will normally issue an Improvement Notice which requires the employer to sort things out within a reasonable time. If there is a serious risk to health and safety, however, it is possible for an inspector to issue a Prohibition Notice to stop certain hazardous activities. Another body responsible for aspects of health and safety in general practice is the local Fire Authority, which has powers of entry and is required to inspect some buildings for the purpose of issuing fire certificates. They may, in certain circumstances, exercise powers similar to HSE inspectors.

In addition to these duties, every employer with more than five staff has to have a statement of health and safety policy, and arrangements for carrying out that policy. This is to help ensure that safe systems and practices are developed, and that staff are involved and understand their responsibilities. Where there is a recognised trade union, then it can appoint health and safety representatives who the employer has to consult on all health and safety issues, and who will carry out inspections of the premises in order to ensure there are no hazards to their fellow members of staff.

Employers also have obligations to ensure that the community at large is not damaged by the way they carry on their business. A GP must ensure, as far as is reasonably practicable, that any of his/her patients using the premises can have safe access to it. This may be particularly important, as many of the GP's visitors will be elderly or infirm.

Duties are not simply imposed on the employer, however. Members of staff also have obligations which, while not as numerous as of those of the employer, are important. The proper execution of these obligations is essential if the employer is to comply with the law. Failure by an employee to carry out his/her health and safety obligations could, in extreme circumstances, lead to prosecution of the employee. While an employee is at work s/he has to take reasonable care, not only of his/her own health and safety, but also that of any other person who may be affected by his/her activities. Where employees are asked to do something by their employer in order to comply with health and safety requirements, the employees have a duty to co-operate so as to ensure that the health and safety responsibility is complied with.

It is not possible to review all the statutory instruments made in connection with health and safety. Some are specific to other areas of activity (e.g. harbours and docks), others relate to occupational diseases which are unlikely to arise in employment in general practice, such as pneumoconiosis. In the health service, the *Ionising Radiation Regulations* and the *Asbestos Regulations* may well be significant, as X-ray equipment and other radiation sources are widespread and asbestos is used in many older large buildings. However, many are of direct and continuing relevance to general practice and some of these are considered below.

REPORTING OF INJURIES, DISEASES AND DANGEROUS OCCURRENCES REGULATIONS 1985

Where any person dies or suffers serious injuries as a result of an accident in connection with work, then there is an obligation to report it immediately to the enforcing authority (usually the local authority); and where less serious injury leads to an absence of more than three days, a report must be made within a week.

Where there is any such reportable event, the employer has to ensure that details of it are recorded in a record book kept on the premises. The date and time of the incident must be recorded together with the full name, occupation and nature of the injury to the person affected, a brief description of the circumstances of the incident and details of the place where the incident occurred.

CONTROL OF SUBSTANCES HAZARDOUS TO HEALTH REGULATIONS (COSHH) 1988

These regulations cover a very wide range of material. They cover any form of substance, whether gases or solids, and any type of material, including bacteria and viruses, that are capable of damaging health through being absorbed, injected, inhaled or ingested and which may be encountered at the workplace. The employer is under a duty to ensure that exposure of individuals to the hazardous substance is prevented or, if this is not reasonably practicable, adequately controlled. An employer cannot carry out any work which involves exposure unless, *'he has made a suitable and sufficient assessment of the risks created by that work to the health of those employees and of the steps that need to be taken to meet the requirements of these regulations'*. In addition to this assessment, s/he needs to carry out health surveillance, exposure monitoring and the use of control measures. Most importantly, an employer who exposes any of his/her employees to these substances is obliged to provide that employee with suitable and sufficient information, instructions and training to know the risks to health created by such exposure and the precautions that should be taken. In general practice, one of the key issues is the exposure of individuals to blood-borne pathogens; the following of an appropriate code of practice, such as the BMA code on the use and disposal of sharps, should be sufficient to ensure protection of staff. In addition to the health and safety legislation, there are strict regulations covering the handling and disposal of clinical waste, such as blood-stained bandages, and other material which may create a hazard. As well as the infection hazard, a GP's surgery may contain various chemicals which need to be handled in accordance with COSHH.

THE 'SIX PACK' OF HEALTH AND SAFETY REGULATIONS

Six sets of regulations became effective on 1 January 1993. The key feature of all six was the requirement placed on employers to assess risks to health and safety, and to take measures to reduce any risks. Similarly, employees are under a duty to co-operate and assist employers in implementing the regulations.

1. The Management of Health and Safety at Work Regulations

These require employers to conduct and report assessments of risks to health and safety at work of their employees. Employers are then required to take all practicable steps to eliminate the identified risks and to set up procedures for dealing with serious ones. In addition, they must train staff and supply relevant health and safety information to employees. This 'risk assessment' is fundamental in all health and safety work. In general practice surgeries, there may be many hazards associated with the equipment used and the procedures carried out. However, in addition to these there are very general hazards which will affect every workplace (see Table 6).

2. The Personal Protective Equipment at Work Regulations

These require employers to provide employees with personal protective equipment appropriate to health and safety risks in their work, except where other measures to eliminate these risks have been implemented. In a GP's surgery, an obvious example of this would be ensuring that all members of staff who need them had access to gloves.

3. The Management and Use of Work Equipment Regulations

These require employers to assess the risk to health and safety caused by work equipment, including the risk generated by cleaning and maintaining the equipment. The regulations require minimum standards to be met with respect to emergency procedures and the machinery's controls. In general practice, one

TABLE 6. A WALK AROUND THE SURGERY.

A brief walk around any place of employment may well reveal a variety of hazards which expose individuals to the dangers of a fall, for example:

- A frayed doormat or carpet could lead to a heel or toe becoming caught and an individual tripping.
- The failure to dry the floor after a spillage or a situation where staff have to walk across a recently washed floor exposes them to the danger of slipping.
- Steep or uneven stairs can lead to falls.
- Cluttered floors, trailing wires and open drawers or cupboards make it harder to move safely around the work place.
- Inadequate or inappropriate lighting may mean that an employee does not see a hazard until it is too late.

common source of hazard is poorly adjusted and maintained autoclaves and sterilisers. Under these regulations, GPs have to ensure that the equipment is, and continues to be, safe and used in a safe way.

4. The Display Screen Equipment Regulations

These deal with the working arrangements for computers and word processors. They require employers to modify work stations, work equipment and working practices to eliminate risks to health and safety of employees using display screen equipment. There is a requirement to ensure that employers are provided with appropriate eye sight tests. The employer is also required to *'so plan the activities of users at work in his undertaking that their daily work on display screen equipment is periodically interrupted by such breaks or changes of activity as to reduce their workload to that equipment'*.

5. The Manual Handling Regulations

These require employers to assess the health and safety risk to their employees at work while lifting and handling, and to take all practicable steps to eliminate the identified risks. Where staff may need to assist patients, it may well be that some form of training in lifting is necessary.

6. The Work Place (Health, Safety and Welfare) Regulations

These require employers to assess the risk to the health and safety of their employees in the workplace. They lay down minimum requirements with respect to equipment, ventilation, temperature, lighting, cleanliness, work space, windows, traffic routes, sanitary conditions, eating facilities and changing areas. These regulations apply to employers of five or more staff.

VIOLENCE

One issue of major concern in many general practices is the level of threat from some patients. The Health and Safety Executive's definition of violence is: *'any incident in which an employee is abused, threatened or assaulted by a member of the public in circumstances arising out of the course of his/her employment'*. Violence is a key area where consultation with staff and information gathering are essential. A variety of steps may be taken to discourage violence; these include training employees, changing the layout of waiting areas, providing more information to patients, installing alarm buttons and so on. The policy for dealing with violence should be included in the health and safety policy statement so that all employees are aware of it, co-operate with it and report any incidents. An individual who has been assaulted will be able to claim compensation from the attacker or (more usefully) may make a claim for compensation from the Criminal Injuries Compensation Authority (CICA).

EMPLOYMENT, AND HEALTH AND SAFETY

Health and safety is a key issue in employment. On occasions, disputes about health and safety will cause problems between employer and employees. Employment law provides some limited protection to an employee against dismissal in these circumstances. It states that the reason for dismissal will be 'inadmissible', and therefore unfair, where the employee concerned was carrying out proper health and safety activities or, in circumstances of danger which s/he reasonably believed to be serious and imminent, took or proposed to take appropriate steps to protect him/herself or other persons from the danger. It is clearly in the interest of both employer and employees that there is real understanding of health and safety issues in the work force, and that problems can be addressed in a spirit of co-operation rather than confrontation.

Chapter 7

DOCTORS AND COURTS

Dealing with courts and lawyers is a normal part of clinical practice. Although many regret the fact, the gravity and importance of medical work makes it inevitable that doctors will, from time to time, be involved in matters where they may eventually be required to give evidence. Furthermore, from time to time GPs will be under a professional obligation to report matters to public authorities which may well involve subsequently giving evidence. Courts vary considerably in their procedures and discharge many different functions. The system has evolved and not been designed. Reform has tended to be piecemeal rather than systematic. The procedure in a Coroner's court is inquisitorial; i.e. the coroner decides who should be called and asks most of the questions. In other courts, procedure is adversarial; i.e. plaintiff/prosecution and defendant attempt to establish one view of the facts or cast doubts on another. A coroner may sit with or without a jury. In civil courts (except for a very few matters) the jury has been abolished. A criminal case may be tried by a single professional magistrate, a bench of lay magistrates or a judge sitting with a jury.

ATTENDING COURT

A GP may be before the court as a party to proceedings or as a witness; in this chapter the focus is on the doctor as a witness. In this capacity, doctors should bear in mind that in giving evidence in court they are there to help the court. They should therefore ensure that they retain their impartiality and independence of the parties, and adopt an approach of detached objectivity. There are in essence two sorts of witness - an ordinary witness and an expert witness. An ordinary witness is a witness as to fact, for example a GP who sees a crime being committed might give evidence. More frequently, GPs will be called to give evidence with respect to patients whom they have treated following an assault. Here, they might give evidence of identification, the injuries observed and the treatment given. Although the GP is a witness, the evidence s/he gives arises out of his/her clinical work and s/he is known as a professional witness. An expert witness is called by one party to the proceedings to give an expert interpretation of the facts. Experts' participation in the case is therefore voluntary, but if they accept the obligation to prepare evidence then they also accept the obligation, if required, to appear in court.

It is preferable if doctors can ensure that they have close liaison with the solicitor so that they are kept fully informed of progress and consulted with respect to availability for hearing dates. There is joint BMA/Law Society guidance covering this and other issues with respect to medical evidence. Listing of cases depends on the venue for trial, with different procedures applying in the different courts. Frequently, cases are in a warned list; this means that they may be heard during a specific period. This uncertainty is highly frustrating for all parties to the proceedings. If a solicitor is concerned that a witness may not attend court then s/he may ask the court to issue a witness summons (for criminal cases) or a subpoena (for civil cases). These are orders of the court requiring the witness to attend court on a specific date. If a doctor has a problem with the date s/he should contact the listing officer of the court as quickly as possible since failure to comply with these orders amounts to contempt of court. Effective liaison with the solicitor should ensure that such problems are largely avoided.

REPORTS AND REQUESTS FOR INFORMATION

Where doctors receive requests for information or the release of the medical records relating to a patient, they should first determine whether the patient concerned, possessing capacity to do so, has given express consent to that release of information. If the GP is satisfied as to consent, then consideration should be given to the *Access to Health Records Act* 1990 (considered above), and in particular the provisions with respect to causing harm and disclosing third party information. However, as a general approach a doctor will wish to comply with a patient's request for the release of records for the purpose of litigation since to do so is to act in accordance with the patient's interests. Where there is any question of proceedings for clinical negligence, GPs should consult their defence society as soon as possible. The court can order disclosure of medical records under Section 33 of the *Supreme Court Act* 1981 before any proceedings are launched, and under Section 34 after proceedings have been issued. In the light of this, and the access provisions, doctors are generally encouraged to release records, preferably to another doctor, where there is a question of harm to the patient's well-being. Since GPs are under an obligation to continue to provide care to such patients, they may seek to negotiate that copies rather than original notes are sent; they are entitled to charge a reasonable sum for photocopying.

Where GPs are asked to prepare reports, it is important that they know what information is required to avoid irrelevant and tendentious comment. A report should firstly identify the doctor and his/her qualifications and appointments, and then give details of the patient, the date of examination and whether any witnesses were present at the time. The report should set out the facts established by the examination, together with a comment on the general health of the individual and as much history as is necessary. Any opinion should be restricted to relevant issues; for example, whether the injuries present are consistent with the explanation of their cause.

The police are not entitled to information concerning a doctor's patients, and the release of such information is a breach of confidentiality which may need to be justified. However, in England and Wales, under the *Police and Criminal Evidence Act* 1984, the police may apply to a circuit judge for permission to seize 'all documentary and other records' relating to a person's physical or mental health. In Scotland the police have wider powers.

The general ethical obligation of confidentiality is discussed elsewhere (see Chapter 3). However, two areas of disclosure without consent are so closely tied to the effective working of the courts and the work of general practice as to merit further discussion here - the position with respect to death, and the conflicts which may arise with respect to children.

CORONERS' COURTS

The responsibilities of a coroner include, under Section 3(1) of the *Coroners Act 1887*, the duty to hold an inquest when s/he is informed:

> 'that the dead body of a person is lying within his jurisdiction, and there is reasonable cause to suspect that such person has died either a violent or an unnatural death, or has died a sudden death of which the cause is unknown, or that such person has died in prison, or in such place or under such circumstances as to require an inquest in pursuance of any Act.'

It is accepted practice for GPs to report to the coroner any cases of doubt or suspicion. These include:

- where an accident in any way contributed to the cause of death, e.g. where septicaemia has set in;
- death related to chronic or acute alcoholism, poisoning, or drug or substance abuse;
- death where drug therapy, anaesthesia or a surgical procedure may have contributed to death;
- stillbirths where there was a possibility of the child being born alive;
- death where the deceased suffered from an industrial disease, or was in receipt of a disability or war pension;
- death of a foster child;
- death where ill-treatment or neglect hastened death.

In the case of sudden death where the cause is unknown, the coroner is entitled to dispense with an inquest if, after a postmortem, s/he is satisfied that death was due to natural causes. The statute empowers the coroner to call doctors to give evidence and to order postmortems. Specifically, the coroner can summon the doctor who last treated the patient to the inquest to give evidence as to how the patient came to his/her death. Where there is any question of medical misadventure or negligence, doctors should contact their defence body.

CHILDREN

Questions as to the possible need to protect children from the conduct of those who have care of them raise many difficulties for GPs. These include such issues as the conflict between the duty to the child and to other members of the family who are patients, the maintenance of confidentiality in case conferences, the uncertainty of any diagnosis and as to the best course of action.

The Children Act 1989 brought into existence a unified jurisdiction for determining questions relating to the care and upbringing of children. It is founded on the principle that the child's welfare is paramount whenever the court determines a question with respect to the upbringing of a child. In order for the decision-making to be well-informed, it is clearly desirable that the GP has an input at all stages of the child protection procedure. GPs have a fundamental role in diagnosing and preventing abuse.

The GMC blue book provides (paragraph 83):

> *'Deciding whether or not to disclose information is particularly difficult in cases where a patient cannot be judged capable of giving or withholding consent to disclosure. One such situation may arise where a doctor believes that a patient may be a victim of abuse or neglect. In such circumstances the patient's interests are paramount and will usually require the doctor to disclose relevant information to an appropriate, responsible person or an officer of a statutory agency.'*

Such disclosure would usually be to the local social services authority who have statutory responsibilities with respect to child protection. Clearly, in cases such as this, if GPs are in doubt they should seek advice from colleagues, their defence society or the BMA.

In handling issues of child abuse, much emphasis is placed on the importance of effective inter-agency working so that all relevant information is properly gathered and considered. The Department of Health (DoH) has issued guidance making it clear that all those in receipt of medical information at a case conference are under an obligation of confidentiality. The first and foremost consideration must be the interest of the child, and that will usually override the general rule of professional confidence. Where it becomes necessary to give information about other members of the family, consideration may be given to restricting the number of recipients of that information; this question will need to be addressed on a case-by-case basis in the light of the DoH and professional guidance.

FEES

Doctors often complain about the delay in resolving questions of fees in cases in which they are involved. The level of fee which may be payable depends on the nature of the witness. If a doctor is there as a professional witness, i.e. a witness as to fact dealing with a matter which arose in his/her professional practice, then the Lord Chancellor's Department and legal aid recognise this, and there is provision for a higher rate of fees than is normally paid to witnesses. Where a doctor is an expert and thus a volunteer, the schedules used as guidance by Legal Aid and the Crown Prosecution Service reflect this.

In civil proceedings, doctors should try to arrange that their fees are agreed in advance and paid as the work proceeds. Where a solicitor is acting under the legal aid scheme, this is still possible as the solicitor can seek prior approval from the Legal Aid Board. It is therefore not necessary to wait until the end of the case to pay the doctor's fees. In non-legal aid cases, the solicitor should pay the bills as they are presented. Where there is a dispute over the payment of fees, a doctor can seek the intervention of the Solicitors' Complaints Bureau; however, if there is only an agreement to pay 'reasonable costs', then the Bureau is unable to assist, and in default of agreement the only recourse is to the courts.

In criminal cases, it is normally necessary to wait for the conclusion of the case for payment for preparation work. The attendance expenses and fee are claimed from the court and are subject to guidance issued by the Lord Chancellor.

If possible, doctors should negotiate with solicitors a provision that if a court hearing is cancelled at short notice (e.g. 48 hours) a proportion of the fee for the hearing should be payable. This should compensate for the expense of re-arranging commitments and hiring a locum.

The BMA provides guidance to members on how they should approach the difficult question of setting fees for this sort of work.

As a general principle, the Law Society advises its members:

'Unless there is agreement to the contrary, a solicitor is personally responsible for paying the proper costs of any professional agent or other person whom he instructs on behalf of his client, whether or not he receives payment by his client.'

Conclusion

Courts, in all their many forms, are generally distinguished by their apparent ability to consume (or waste) enormous amounts of time. Doctors should help the courts by being clear about their role, and should work with lawyers to ensure that their time is used effectively. This way they are best able to discharge their obligations to their patients, and also their obligation to society at large to assist in the fair and effective administration of justice.

Chapter 8

DOCTORS AND THE MEDIA

Doctors are considered important figures in their local communities, and will sometimes be called upon by the press and local broadcasters to make comments on issues of public concern. This is especially true of doctors who are members of an LMC (local medical committee), or who hold other offices and are seen as spokesmen for the profession.

As such, there is a fund of goodwill and respect on the part of both the media and the public. There is, consequently, a substantial opportunity to inform public debate and educate the public, both in personal health matters and in questions of local and national health policy.

If a doctor is approached for a comment or to give an interview, then, providing it is professionally appropriate to do so, the doctor should consider the request carefully. Before agreeing, s/he should establish:

- what the interview will cover and how long it will be;

- the context of the programme and whether anyone else will be interviewed;

- the logistics - live or recorded, and when and where the interview will take place.

If doctors agree to be interviewed, they should prepare carefully and know the key points to get across. They should be positive, confident and straightforward, and should avoid getting distracted into side issues or talking too much. Above all, they should bear in mind the audience they are trying to reach and the likely impact of the interview on them.

The GMC guidance on advertising should be taken into account in contacts with the media. Where a doctor is appearing as a spokesman, no problems arise. Care should be taken to ensure that, where a doctor is broadcasting or writing on clinical issues, no implication arises that there is a recommendation to consult that particular doctor. Where a doctor appears regularly advising on medical matters, the GMC states:

'It should be explicitly stated that the doctor cannot offer individual advice or see individual patients as a result.'

The position is different, and potentially more difficult, where the doctor is professionally involved in a news story. This could happen in a variety of ways, but commonly arises when an individual patient is unable to obtain treatment which s/he (and the GP) think appropriate. Here, where the patient has consented to a discussion of the need for medical treatment, the GP may be cast in the dual roles of advocate on behalf of the patient and of explaining the context of the difficulty in terms of the availability of resources and other questions. In other cases, particularly those involving children, actual or potential court proceedings (where issues of contempt of court arise) or where the conduct or competence of the doctor is in question, it will rarely be appropriate to make any public statement; advice should always be sought beforehand.

DEFAMATION

In any communication an individual makes to one person, which deals with the affairs of another, there is a danger (however remote) that the communication will be defamatory. This area of law is one of the most complex and unsatisfactory of all; so much so that there is not even a clear definition of what defamation is. A partial definition is that:

> 'A *statement may be defamatory if it would tend to lower an individual's reputation in the eyes of right-thinking members of society generally or which tends to cause him to be shunned or which brings him into hatred, ridicule or contempt or which tends to discredit him in his profession or trade.*'

In broad terms, libel is the written or broadcast word and slander is spoken. Slander is actionable only if the plaintiff can establish that s/he has suffered an actual loss - usually of some measurable financial benefit.

One point worth noting in this definition is that any statement about an individual which would cause him to be shunned is defamatory. The values of society may not be as charitable and fair-minded as one would wish, and various plaintiffs have, over the years, successfully pursued actions for defamation where it was incorrectly alleged that the plaintiff was insolvent, insane or suffering from a contagious disease, or that a woman had been raped. In cases such as these, a jury would have to decide whether or not such an allegation would cause the individual to be shunned and avoided.

A plaintiff in defamation proceedings has to show that the words complained of were defamatory, referred to him/her and were published by the defendant. When s/he has done that, the defendant needs to establish a defence in order to escape liability.

Among the defences to a claim of defamation are:

- justification,
- fair comment on a matter of public interest,
- qualified and absolute privilege.

A statement is justified if it is true; however, the burden of proving the truth of a statement falls upon the individual who asserts that truth, and this may not be easy to do where the 'truth' is known through rumour. Fair comment protects the honest expression of opinion - however unreasonable. The difficulty with the defence is that it only covers comment. These comments have to be based on some facts which need to be referred to in the article.

There are certain circumstances where false statements about another do not give rise to liability. These are where the statement is fairly made in the discharge of a public or private duty, whether legal or moral, or in the conduct of the person's own affairs; in some matter where his/her interest is concerned. If the statement is *'fairly warranted by any reasonable occasion or exigency, and*

honestly made, such communications are protected for the common convenience and welfare of society; and the law has not restricted the right to make them within any narrow limits'. This defence is defeated by showing that the defendant knew that what s/he said was false. Absolute privilege attaches to statements made as a witness in court proceedings. This means that under no circumstances can defamation proceedings be brought against the witness for those statements (although the situation is very different if they are repeated outside the court!).

Doctors have, from time to time, appeared as plaintiffs in the libel courts. Over the years, the courts have established that it is defamatory to state that a doctor lacks ability, qualifications, knowledge, skill, judgement or efficiency in his/her professional work. It is clearly defamatory to say that s/he has caused the death or illness of a patient due to careless, incompetent or reckless treatment, or that s/he has shown gross ignorance in his/her treatment of a patient or unprofessional conduct in the treatment of a case.

Frequently, doctors feel highly aggrieved that a patient has complained about them. At the end of a traumatic service committee hearing, a doctor may feel that s/he is vindicated and has demonstrated that the complaint was completely unfounded and false, and may wonder whether to bring proceedings in defamation. It is almost invariably wholly inappropriate to do so. The complaint and the hearing will attract qualified privilege; it will be very hard to show that the patient did not believe the truth of the complaint. The mental state or anguish of the complainant at the time the complaint was made will often be such as to render it impossible for a jury to satisfy itself as to the requisite intention to defeat privilege. The defendant will, in most circumstances, be of very inadequate means and be unable to meet any judgement; this could well leave a plaintiff doctor bearing substantial costs. Finally, it is unlikely to assist the doctor with his/her other patients if s/he is known to be suing one of them. In any circumstance where doctors feel they have been libelled, they should take careful advice before acting.

COMMENTING ON COLLEAGUES

Doctors will, from time to time, be called upon to comment on their colleagues' performance or conduct. The GMC has published advice on this problem in both its aspects: when to speak and when to remain silent (Figure 8). This advice reflects both the nature and needs of professional obligations, and also the impact of the law of defamation upon these duties. It emphasises the conflicting demands which it is of the essence of good professional practice to resolve. Doctors must recognise, however, that what they may view as a proper discharge of their responsibility to report under paragraph 63, other people concerned will view as *'gratuitous and unsustainable comment'*. In cases such as this, *'off the record comments'* are clearly inappropriate. The practical advice must be that a measured statement made after a careful appraisal of the evidence available to an appropriate person (not to the world at large) will not give grounds for a successful claim in defamation against the person making the statement.

FIGURE 8 - GMC ADVICE ON 'COMMENT ABOUT PROFESSIONAL COLLEAGUES'

62. Doctors are frequently asked to express a view about a colleague's professional practice. This may, for example, happen in the course of medical audit or peer review procedure, or when a doctor is asked to give a reference about a colleague. It may also occur in a less direct and explicit way when a patient seeks a second opinion, specialist advice or an alternative form of treatment. Honest comment is entirely acceptable in such circumstances, provided it is carefully considered and can be justified, that it is offered in good faith and that it is intended to promote the best interests of patients.

63. Further, it is any doctor's duty, where the circumstances so warrant, to inform an appropriate person or authority about a colleague whose professional performance appears to be in some way deficient. Arrangements exist to deal with such problems, and they must be used in order to ensure that high standards of medical practice are maintained.

64. However, gratuitous and unsustainable comment which, whether directly or by implication, sets out to undermine trust in a professional colleague's knowledge or skills, is unethical.

(From GMC Professional Conduct and Discipline: Fitness to Practise)

Chapter 9

THE PATIENTS' CHARTER

The *Patients' Charter* was announced by the Government at the end of 1991. It is intended to explain to patients how the NHS works, so that they can get the best possible service out of it; it is also intended by the Government to enable patients to put pressure on the NHS, so that it is more responsive to the wishes of patients. The initial Charter emphasised certain existing rights with respect to the NHS:

- Care on the basis of need, not ability to pay.
- To be registered with a GP.
- To receive emergency medical care at any time.
- To be referred to a consultant when the GP thinks it is necessary, and to be referred for a second opinion if the patient and the GP consider it desirable.
- To be given a clear explanation of any treatment proposed, including its risks and any alternatives before the patient decides whether or not to be treated.
- To have access to the patient's health records, knowing that they are kept confidential by the NHS.
- To choose whether or not to take part in research or teaching.

In addition, the Government sought to introduce new 'rights'; these related to information, waiting for hospital treatment and the handling of complaints in the NHS. It further set out 'National Charter Standards' with respect to services.

One problem with this approach has been that many of these 'rights' or 'standards', while desirable, are not attainable by the service. While they are not attainable, there is often no effective course of action that the patient can take. This process of raising expectations in circumstances where it may not be possible to meet them has caused, over the past two years, a very rapid increase in the level of formal complaints received by FHSAs against doctors and, in turn, a great increase in the number of service committee hearings.

However, in addition to these 'rights' and the provisions of the *NHS Act* under which the patient may expect to receive treatment, many of the charters cover issues considered in this book. The charters deal with questions of consent to treatment, confidentiality of patient information and access to patients' records (Chapter 3). They deal with the quality of service which a patient may expect (considered as a question of professional discipline in Chapter 2, as a NHS obligation in Chapter 1 and as the law of negligence in Chapter 4). The right of patients to receive treatment which is sensitive to the needs of members of ethnic minority communities is good practice, supported by the principles of non-discrimination set out in the *Race Relations Act* (considered in Chapter 1). Where charters speak of premises standards, they are usually relying on existing obligations of occupiers of premises and employers of staff to people who visit their premises (Chapter 6). It may be seen, therefore, that much of what is being attempted by the Government is to explain to individuals what their entitlements are in one simple document. It is perhaps not surprising that some confusion has arisen, especially since the charters are intended by the Government to be a means by which patients can put pressure on the health service to provide better care.

Since the initial Charter, there have been initiatives, at both national and local level, to generate charters with a respect to individual health authorities. In particular, there is encouragement for FHSAs to work with GPs to develop local charters covering the full range of family health services. It is intended that these charters spring from a voluntary commitment for the individuals concerned to provide a clearly specified quality of service to patients. However, *'no undue pressure should be brought to bear on practices which decided they do not wish to enter into commitments outwith the GP's Terms of Service'* (see Figure 9).

FIGURE 9 - PATIENTS' RIGHTS IN THE GENERAL MEDICAL SERVICES

Whether or not the practice has developed a local 'charter', patients have the right to:

(1)	Be registered with a GP.
(2)	Change doctors easily and quickly.
(3)	Be offered a health check on joining the doctor's list for the first time.
(4)	Receive emergency care at any time through a family practitioner.
(5)	Have appropriate drugs and medicines prescribed.
(6)	Be referred to a consultant acceptable to them when their GP thinks it necessary, and be referred for a second opinion if they and the GP agree this is desirable.
(7)	Have access to their medical health records, subject to any limitations in the law, and to know that those working for the NHS are under a legal duty to keep their contents confidential.
(8)	Choose whether or not to take part in medical research or medical training.
(9)	If between 16 and 74 they have not seen their doctor in the previous three years, to have the health check to which they are entitled and to the existing health promotion arrangements, and to be offered a yearly home visit and health check if 75 years old or over.
(10)	Be given detailed information about local family doctor services through their FHSA's local directory.
(11)	Receive a copy of their doctor's practice leaflet, setting out the service he or she provides.
(12)	Receive a full and prompt reply to any complaints they make about NHS services.

(From NHS Management Executive letter EL(92)88)

Where there are local charters, key issues that should be addressed include statements about how quickly patients can expect access to health care, how quickly they should be able to contact the service, and information about the procedures for dealing with comments, suggestions and complaints.

There are many other areas which local charters could cover, including services for minorities, development of health promotion programmes, handling of test results, and the quality and effectiveness of communications.

In order for practice staff to be able to deal effectively with patients, it is important that they understand what patients expect from the practice. This is clearly shaped by patients' understanding of health service charters. In order for these charters to be successful in improving health care rather than merely a source of conflict, not only must practice staff understand and work effectively with the charters, but there must be clear communication by the practice with patients so that all patients understand how to use the health service smoothly and effectively. A knowledge of the law underlying the charters should help staff to achieve this.

A GLOSSARY
OF HEALTH
SERVICE BODIES

Association of Medical Secretaries, Practice Administrators and Receptionists (AMSPAR)

A charity concerned with the advancement of the learning and skill of certain groups of staff in general practice.

British Medical Association (BMA)

The BMA is an association of doctors concerned with the promotion of the science of medicine, and the maintenance of the honour and interest of the medical profession. It is a professional association and trade union, and represents doctors in all parts of the NHS. In addition, it advises doctors on a wide range of professional matters, and publishes the *British Medical Journal* (BMJ).

Community Health Council (CHC)

These are bodies set up in each area under the NHS Acts to represent the interest of consumers of this service to health authorities.

Department of Health (DoH)

This is responsible for national planning and objective setting within the NHS, the allocation of resources and monitoring of performance. It delegates responsibilities to Regional Health Authorities (RHAs). The minister in charge - The Secretary of State for Health - is accountable to Parliament for the actions of the Department of Health. In Wales, Scotland and Northern Ireland the functions of the DoH are discharged by the appropriate government department (i.e. Welsh Office, Scottish Office or Northern Ireland Office), and the relevant Secretary of State is accountable to Parliament for the health service in Wales, Scotland and Northern Ireland.

District Health Authority (DHA)

Each DHA is responsible for assessing the needs of its local population and the planning, development and purchasing of health services in its district in accordance with the guidelines it receives from the department and the RHA, and within its allocated budget.

Family Health Services Authority (FHSA)

These are responsible for the provision of family practitioner services (general medical and dental services, pharmaceutical and ophthalmic services). They enter into contracts with individual practitioners, and administer the *Terms of Service* and the *Statement of fees and allowances*. They are responsible for service committees which consider allegations of breach of *Terms of Service* by general practitioners. They collaborate with DHAs in planning and purchasing services and developing GP premises. The Government proposes to merge DHAs and FHSAs. To do this it will have to introduce a new Act of Parliament.

General Medical Council (GMC)

This was first set up in the 19th century. Its role is now defined by the *Medical Act* 1983. It registers doctors, co-ordinates medical education, and provides advice on standards of professional conduct and medical ethics. It administers professional discipline, and also deals with cases where a doctor's ability to practise is seriously impaired by his/her physical or mental condition.

General Medical Service Committee (GMSC)

This is the committee of the BMA responsible for representing the interests of general practitioners at a national level. It is formed mainly of representatives of LMCs.

Health Board (HB)

Health Boards are responsible, in Scotland and Northern Ireland, for the functions which in England and Wales are discharged by FHSAs and DHAs.

Health Education Authority (HEA)

The HEA is a special health authority in England responsible for providing information and advice about health to members of the public, and assisting doctors to do the same.

Health and Safety Executive (HSE)

The HSE is responsible for maintaining high standards of health and safety in the workplace, investigating accidents, and providing guidance and advice.

Local Medical Committee (LMC)

LMCs are committees of general practitioners in the area of an FHSA or Health Board, which are recognised by the NHS as representing GPs, and which are entitled to be consulted on matters affecting the delivery of general medical services in the area.

Medical defence organisations

These are the Medical and Dental Defence Union of Scotland (MDDUS), the Medical Defence Union (MDU) and the Medical Protection Society (MPS). They are professional associations advising doctors on professional issues, and assisting them with complaints and negligence claims arising from their clinical practice. All GPs are members of one or other of them, as they provide indemnity for any costs and damages awarded in a medical negligence action. Under the *Terms of Service* of GPs, cover of this sort is necessary.

Medical Practices Committee (MPC)

The Medical Practices Committee considers applications from doctors to provide general medical services, and decides whether or not a doctor may go into practice in any particular area.

National Health Service (NHS)

The NHS aims to provide a comprehensive health-care service, including hospital and specialist services, general medical services, dental and ophthalmic services, pharmaceutical services, community health services and school health services. The bulk of these services are free of charge.

NHS Executive

The NHS Executive is responsible for the operation and management of the NHS within the Department of Health. It sets objectives for health authorities in line with government policies and within the given resources, and monitors the performance of NHS Trusts.

NHS Trust

These are the bodies set up under the *NHS and the Community Care Act* to manage the hospitals and other facilities or groups of staff which directly provide services to patients under contract with DHAs and GP fundholders.

Regional Health Authority (RHA)

RHAs are the link between the NHS management nationally and DHAs and FHSAs. They set objectives for DHAs and FHSAs, allocate resources to DHAs, FHSAs and GP fundholders and monitor the performance of DHAs and FHSAs. The Government intends to abolish RHAs and give their functions to regional outposts of the NHS Executive. This will require an Act of Parliament.

Royal College of General Practitioners (RCGP)

This body, working under a Royal Charter, seeks to encourage, foster and maintain the highest possible standards in general practice. Entry is by examination. It promotes education, audit and research in general practice. Similar colleges exist to advance other specialities in medical practice.

Royal College of Midwives (RCM)

This is a professional association and trade union representing and advising midwives.

Royal College of Nursing (RCN)

This is a professional association and trade union representing and advising nurses.

United Kingdom Central Council for Nursing, Midwifery and Health Visiting (UKCC)

This is the statutory body (similar to the GMC) responsible for supervising education, and for registering, advising and disciplining members of these professions.

Unison

This is a trade union representing a wide range of staff within the NHS, including some nurses, administrators, and clerical and ancillary staff.

FURTHER READING

The field of law in general practice is vast, and there are many publications covering different aspects of it. This is simply a list of some of those that may be more readily available and give further information of different aspects of this book.

General practitioners' obligations to patients

The law in general practice edited by D Pickersgill; (Radcliff Medical Press Ltd).

Medicine, patients and the law, Margaret Brazier; (Penguin)

Medical and nursing ethics

Professional Conduct and Discipline; Fitness to Practice (the 'Blue Book'); (GMC)

Code of Professional Conduct for the Nurse, Midwife and Health Visitor; (UKCC).

Rights and Responsibilities of Doctors; (BMA).

Consent, confidentiality, medical records and mental health

Guidance in confidentiality towards people under 16 years is issued by the BMA, GMSC, HEA, Brook Advisory Centres, Family Planning Association and RCGP.

Medical Ethics Today - its Practice and Philosophy; (BMA)

Mental Health Law (B Hoggett)

Medical negligence

There is a large and increasing literature on this area of law. It includes *Medical Law* by I Kennedy and A Grubb; *Medical Negligence* by Powers and Harris; and *Medical Negligence* by Michael Jones.

Doctors and courts

The BMA and the Law Society have produced a handbook, *Medical Evidence: Guidance for Doctors and Lawyers*.

Legal Aspects of Medical Practice; (Bernard Knight)

Employment law

The Advisory Conciliation and Arbitration Service (ACAS) has published codes of conduct and a handbook on various aspects of employment law, but in particular disciplinary procedures. The Commission for Racial Equality (CRE) and the

Equal Opportunities Commission (EOC) publish leaflets in their field, and Trade Unions publish a large amount of guidance in this area. A useful general introduction to the law in this field is:

> Butterworths *Employment Law Guide* edited C Osman
> (Butterworths)

Health and safety

The Health and Safety Executive publishes a large amount of guidance in this area. In addition, trade unions publish advice for safety representatives. Among many general texts available is Tolley's *Health and Safety at Work Handbook* (Tolley).

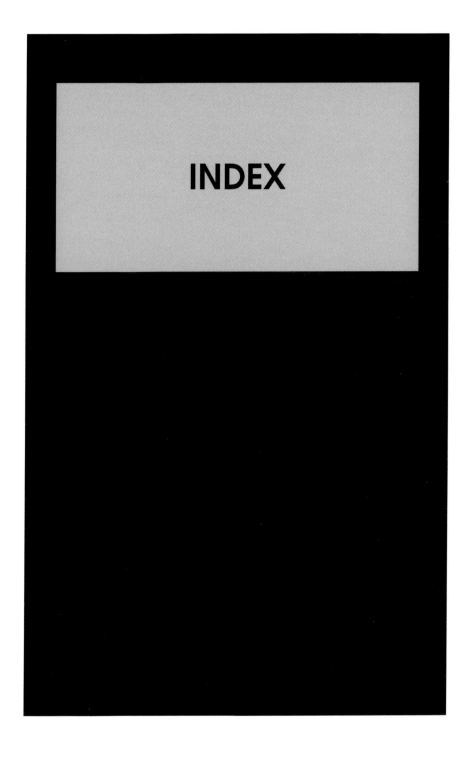

INDEX

A

abortion 18
absolute privilege 72
abuse of patients 23
Acts of Parliament 12, 24, 25, 30, 32, 33, 35, 43, 44, 49, 50, 53, 56, 65, 66, 76, 81, 82

adversarial procedure 64
advertising 70
Advisory Conciliation and Arbitration Service (ACAS) 51, 84
age discrimination 52
alcohol abuse 21, 24
anaesthesia 66
annual reports 15
antenatal care 54
antenatal diagnosis of disability 45
assault 30
attendance expenses 68
autonomy 19, 20

B

beneficence 19, 20
blood-borne pathogens 59

'Blue Book' 16, 67
BMA/Law Society guidelines 64
Bolam test 42
breach of 7, 8, 15, 23, 28, 38, 48, 65
    confidentiality 23, 28, 65
    contract 48
    duty of care 7, 8, 38
    terms of service 15, 80
British Medical Association (BMA) 67, 80, 84
British Medical Journal (BMJ) 80
Brook Advisory Centres 84
burden of proof 40

C

capability 52
care 15, 76
    availability of 15
    on the basis of need 76
cases 38-42
    Bolam v Friern Hospital Management Committee 38
    Cassidy v Ministry of Health 40
    Coles v Reading and District Hospital Management Committee 41
    Gillick 31
    Hotson 40
    Lobley v Going 41
    Prendergast v Sam and Dee Limited 40, 42
    Sa'd v Robinson and Dunlop 42
    Sidaway 39
    Whitehouse v Jordan 39
    Wilsher v Essex AHA 38, 40
certification of illness 13, 15, 21
chemicals - working with 59
child abuse 32, 66, 67
child health surveillance 13
child protection procedure 67
children 30-32, 42, 65, 66-67, 70
civil courts 64
civil liability 30
civil liberties 35
civil proceedings 67
claims for medical negligence 43-44
clinical negligence 65

exposure monitoring 59
eye sight tests 60

F

failure to visit 41
fair comment 71
fair procedures 51
false statements 71
Family Planning Association (FPA) 84
Family Health Services Authority (FHSA) 12, 15, 32, 44, 45, 76, 77, 80, 82
fees 67
financial loss calculation 40, 41, 71
Fire Authority 57
fire certificates 57
fitness to practise 22
foster child death 66
fraud 21

G

General Medical Council (GMC) 15, 15, 16, 18, 19, 21, 24, 25, 29, 70, 72, 81
General Medical Services Committee (GMSC) 12, 34, 81, 84
Geneva Declaration 18-19
GPs 8, 12-16, 19, 20, 25, 32-34, 38, 41, 43-45, 52, 57, 64-68, 76, 77, 80, 82, 84
    accountability to the courts,15-16
    access to premises 57
    capability 52
    courts 64-68
    data protection 33-34
    expenses 15, 68
    failure to visit 41
    fundholders 82
    home visits 13, 20, 41
    ill-health. 16
    legal framework of general practice 8, 12
    medical negligence claims 43-44
    misconduct 16, 19, 52
    NHS 12-16
    obligations to patients 12, 84
    obligations to the FHSA 15
    premises 57, 76, 80
    registration 16, 19, 25
    registration with 76, 77
    responsibilities to staff 14-15
    Terms of Service 13, 14, 20, 32, 38, 41, 45, 77, 80, 81

H

I

itemised pay statement 49

J

judge-made law 7
jury 64
justice 19-20

L

Law Society 68
law 7-9, 16, 40, 48-54, 56, 84-85
    Channel Islands 7
    common 7, 8, 56
    contract 7, 48
    criminal 7
    customary 7
    definition of 7
    discrimination 9
    employment 9, 16, 48-54, 84-85
    Isle of Man 7
    judge-made 7
    Northern Ireland 7
    Scotland 7
    statute 7, 8
    tort 7, 40
    UK 7
legal aid 44, 67
Legal Aid Board 67
legislation 8
libel 71-72
libel courts 72
lighting 60
limitation - personal injury 44
local broadcasters 70
local charters 77-78
Local Medical Committee (LMC) 70, 81
Lord Chancellor's Department 67-68
loss of income 41

M

maternity 9, 13, 51, 53-54
    leave 54
    medical services 13
    rights 9, 51, 53-54

record book - injury 58
recruitment 53
'Red Book' 12
redundancy 48, 50, 52
references 48
referrals 13, 15, 42, 76
Regional Health Authorities (RHAs) 80, 82
registration to practise 19, 25
regular claims 15
regulations 12, 15, 25, 43, 58-60
    Asbestos Regulations 58
    Control of Substances Hazardous to Health Regulations (COSHH) 1988
    58-59
    Display Screen Equipment Regulations 60
    Ionising Radiation Regulations 58
    Management and Use of Work Equipment Regulations 59
    Management of Health and Safety at Work Regulations 59
    Manual Handling Regulations 60
    Medical Devices Regulations 1994 43
    NHS (General Medical Services) Regulations 1992 12
    NHS (Service Comittees and Tribunal) Regulations 1992 15
    Reporting of Injuries Diseases and Dangerous Occurrences Regulations
    1985 58
Nurses Midwives and Health Visitors (Professional Conduct) Rules 1987 25
Personal Protective Equipment at Work Regulations 59
Work Place (Health Safety and Welfare) Regulations 60
research 76
responsible medical officer (RMO) 35
retirement age 51
risk assessment 59
Royal College of General Practitioners (RCGP) 82, 84
Royal College of Midwives (RCM) 82
Royal College of Nursing (RCN) 82

S

safe access to premises 57
safety at work 56-61, 85
sanitary conditions 60
Scottish Office 80
second opinion 73
Second World War 18
Secretary of State for Health 80
self-treatment 22

tort, law of 7, 40
tort of battery 42
tort of negligence 14, 56
trade union membership discrimination 48, 52-53
trade unions 50, 52, 57, 82, 85
training 52, 57, 60
transfer of staff 52
treatment - alternative form of 73

U

UKCC Register - reasons for removal from 23
unconscious patients 30
under-age girls 31
unfair dismissal 48, 50
Unison 82
United Kingdom Central Council for Nursing Midwifery and Health Visiting
(UKCC) 21-22

V

vaccination 13
vicarious liability 15
violence 21, 61
visits 13, 20, 41

W

war pensions 66
warned list 64
Welsh Office 80
witness summons 64
wrongful life 45

X

X-rays 58